Robin Whittle

April '72

WHITTLE

LIFE NATURE LIBRARY

THE
EARTH

LIFE NATURE LIBRARY

THE EARTH

by Arthur Beiser
and The Editors of TIME-LIFE BOOKS

TIME-LIFE INTERNATIONAL (Nederland) N.V.

About the Author

Arthur Beiser, who was born and educated in New York City, has made the study of the earth his career. A geophysicist, he has written 24 books and contributed dozens of articles to scientific journals. A former vice-president of Nuclear Research Associates, Inc., he has been an associate professor of physics at New York University, where he received his B.A., M.S. and Ph.D., and served as chief scientist on expeditions which established cosmic ray and geophysical observatories in the South Pacific, Alaska and Colorado. Among Dr. Beiser's books are *Concepts of Modern Physics*; *Basic Concepts of Physics*; *Mainstream of Physics*; *Fundamentals of Physical Science* and *The Physical Universe* (with Konrad Krauskopf); *Physics for Everybody* and *The Story of Cosmic Rays* (with his wife, Germaine Beiser); and an anthology, *The World of Physics*. His textbooks are used in more than 500 colleges and universities throughout the world.

ON THE COVER: The buttes of Monument Valley in the southwestern U.S.A. glow in the sunset. Hard stone tops saved them from the water erosion which abraded the softer rock all around them.

This international edition adapted by E.W.C. Wilkins.

Contents

Introduction

SERIOUS study of the earth began with increasing world industrialization, largely through the need for more and more mineral raw materials —coal, oil, metals, building materials and water supplies. From this practical and fairly recent beginning, the earth sciences have matured into a history of the earth. This knowledge and these concepts constitute an essential part of the intellectual background of today's understanding and aesthetic appreciation of nature and of man's place in it.

This book is not, nor does it pretend to be, a scientific treatise. Nevertheless, its superb photographs and stimulating text combine to make it a fine introduction to the earth and its processes for the non-professional person who wishes to "read this Book of Earth aright" and, in doing so, to see more clearly man's unceasing efforts to discover greater order, meaning and beauty in the chaos of detailed fact that makes up the natural world.

The story of the earth through the immensities of time is at once difficult and easy to read. No one can comprehend it fully, yet no one can fail to be rewarded for closely observing the scraps of records that lie everywhere about us. Every rock that crops out along the country roadside or in a city park and every feature of the natural landscape offers a host of clues to their origin. This erratic glacial boulder, that exposure of fossiliferous limestone, the alluvial valley of this river, that distant range of mountains—all will yield a wealth of information about various aspects of their history. To be sure, finding the answers to some questions that might be asked about their origin challenges all one's ingenuity, but the meaning of much of the evidence is readily apparent. To become aware of such questions about the way the earth was formed—and aware of the perspective of geological time—is to add a new dimension to one's mind.

The earth sciences are astir. The techniques and concepts of geophysics, geochemistry, biochemistry and other disciplines are being brought to bear increasingly on old questions about the history of rocks and landscapes and on broader problems of the origin of life, the causes of mountains, continents and oceans, and the earth's place in the solar system and the universe. Surprising new facts and unsuspected relationships between facts are being discovered at an increasing rate. Some of the old problems are beginning to yield—at least a little. Man, with his inborn fire, his passion for meaning and order in all things, illuminates the record, and the story of the earth grows more fascinating every year.

WILLIAM W. RUBEY
Emeritus Professor of Geology and Geophysics
University of California
Los Angeles, California

1

A Small but Extraordinary Planet

THIS is a journey to the earth. It begins far out in the immeasurable universe, within a cluster of galaxies that are huddled together in what atronomers call a "local group". One member of this cosmic family, itself made up of countless stars, has a graceful, Catherine-wheel-like form. This is the Milky Way; as galaxies go, it is only of fair-to-middling size, yet its dimensions are numbing to the mind. From edge to edge across its luminous disc, it measures some 100,000 light-years. Its central bulge is as much as 25,000 light-years thick. And one light-year, the distance light travels in a year at the speed of 186,234 miles a second, is a shade under six million million miles.

Some two-thirds of the way from the galactic centre, where the stars thin out, there shines an ordinary, yellowish star. It has plenty of room to move around in, for its nearest neighbour in the Milky Way galaxy lies 24 million million miles away—a distance of more than four light-years—and its next neighbour after that is about two light-years beyond. This lonely star that glows, from far off, as weakly as a fire-fly, is our sun. Among its own attendant family of faithfully circling planets, satellites, asteroids, meteoroids and comets, one oddly matched pair (third from the sun, in terms of distance) is the earth and its moon.

A minor planet bound to an ordinary star in the outskirts of one galaxy among thousands of millions—such is the earth. Approached in this way, from the chill reaches of infinite space, it would be all too easy to miss, a speck almost beneath notice except for one thing: of all the places that conceivably could support human life, the earth is the one and only place we know of that does. Its interior and its skin, its atmosphere and its climate and even its behaviour in space—all of which, together with other attributes, will be examined in this book—form in combination a salubrious environment in which life, and especially intelligent life, flourishes. Until proved otherwise, the earth is the wonder of the universe, a unique sphere with an infinity of its own, encompassing everything from the busy world of the atom to the limitless mind and spirit of man. It may not be insignificant in the cosmic scheme of things after all.

Babylon envisaged the earth as a hollow mountain, supported and surrounded by the sea. Inside the earth lay the dark, dusty realm of the dead. Arching over the earth was the solid firmament, across which moved the sun, moon and stars.

Long before men had any real understanding of the shape or size of this planet that sustained them—much less a knowledge of its humble place in the universe—they felt in their bones that each native valley, sheltered harbour or game-rich plain they lived in was somehow central to the entire cosmic scheme of things. In ancient Greece, all the gods of the universe were thought to dwell on a medium-sized mountain, Olympus, 150 miles from Athens; China, although torn and occupied again and again by successions of barbarians, has always held firmly to the proud title of Central Nation; not many decades ago, Boston's joking claim to be the Hub of the Universe was no joke among many Bostonians. Behind each of these and a hundred similar sentiments lay a certain logic: after all, any man is central to his own circular horizon; any kingdom central to its neighbours; the orb of the earth central in human eyes to the surrounding heavens. It was a long time before anyone really pondered the size of the planet itself. The height of continental mountains and the depths of the ocean trenches were—and are—remarkable enough, even though the vertical measure that separates Everest's crest from the bottom of the Mariana Trench is no more, horizontally, than a comfortable day's hike.

Egypt saw the earth as a reclining god, Keb, covered with vegetation, and the heavens as a gracefully bent goddess, held aloft by the god of the atmosphere. The sun god, shown in the two boats, sailed daily across the heavens into death's night.

THOUGH earlier philosophers had concluded that the earth was a globe, it was not until about 250 B.C. that an Alexandrian Greek, Eratosthenes, exercised geometry on the problem of the earth's total dimension. In Syene, an Egyptian up-river town some 5,000 stadia (500 miles) south of Alexandria, there was a deep, dry well. Eratosthenes learned that at noon on the day of the summer solstice, the sun's light shone directly down the well shaft and lit up the bottom. In Alexandria on that same day, he knew, the noon sun was not vertical, but cast a measurable shadow. The sun being a sufficiently distant source of light to make all its rays virtually parallel, Eratosthenes used a simple geometric calculation to show that the difference in angle between Syene and Alexandria was about one fiftieth of a circle. So 5,000 stadia, multiplied by 50, gave Eratosthenes the first close approximation of the earth's circumference that has come down in history. Translating from stadia to miles, he apparently got a value of some 25,000 miles for circumference (the modern measure at the equator is 24,902) and 8,000 miles for diameter (the modern mean is 7,917 miles).

For such rough measurement, Eratosthenes' achievement was remarkable.

(On the basis of it, another Greek geometrician went so far as to calculate the moon's distance from the earth, also with surprisingly accurate results.) Somehow, the Alexandrian value was later ignored or lost. Thus it was that Columbus, some 1,700 years later, set off westwards around the world to reach the Indies, with a far smaller earth in mind. Despite what folklore says, Columbus knew—as did any other master mariner of his day—that the earth was a sphere; what he did not know was the earth's true size, nor was Eratosthenes' rough value re-established until the global circumnavigations of the 16th century.

T ODAY, thanks especially to the refining measurements that were made in the course of the International Geophysical Year (1957-1958), we are quite sophisticated in our knowledge of the earth's dimensions. Indeed, long before the IGY, men were aware that the earth, although spherical, was no perfect sphere. Even before this fact was demonstrated by measurement, Isaac Newton had predicted it—partly on the ground that the more-than-1,000-miles-an-hour velocity of the earth's equatorial region must have some centrifugal effect, and partly on the visual evidence of Jupiter's and Saturn's bulging equators. Field work in the 18th century confirmed Newton's prediction—at the equator the earth is 26.7 miles thicker than it is when measured from pole to pole. Even more exact measurements, based on the movements of America's IGY Vanguard I satellite, have shown that the equatorial bulge is not exactly symmetrical and that its highest points (a matter of 25 feet) lie a little to the south of the earth's equatorial mid-line.

These refinements have led some writers to abandon the classical description of the earth's shape as an "oblate (flattened) spheroid" and grope, instead, with such similes as "pear-shaped". Again, the dominance of vertical measurements over men's imaginations seems to be at work. If all our planet's dimensions were shrunk at once, so that we could inspect a manageable sphere—say five feet across—the human eye could not detect the difference, approximately a fifth of an inch, between equatorial and polar diameters. At the same time, the earth's eye-catching verticalities would vanish. A fine coat of paint would be thicker than the continents' average height above sea level, and a light pin-prick would probe this mock earth's crust more deeply than have man's most ambitious drilling schemes.

By now, an abundance of photographs and verbal accounts from travellers into space testify that the sheer spectacle of the earth lying against the velvety back-drop of space more than compensates for any disappointment over the globe's surpassing smoothness. Even to an extraterrestrial being, little Earth would probably be one of the most beautiful sights in the universe. Perhaps a homeward-bound Martian would thrill more to the sight of the grey and reddish-brown desert textures and amorphous swirls of Mars. But surely he would gape at Earth's outline glow of blue in back-lighting, and the blues, whites and greens of the clouds, water and vegetation that make our planet so unique a sight—at least in our solar system.

To a Martian explorer large events on earth would be easy to follow from fairly far out in space. The annual cycle of vegetation is reflected in colour changes on the continents, and it would be possible to trace the seasonal advance and retreat of snow cover in the high latitudes of the Northern Hemisphere. Clouds are conspicuous, often arrayed in long lines with clear

Hindu conceptions of the earth vary, but one tribe believed that the earth was held up by elephants, whose shiftings caused earthquakes. The elephants stood on a turtle, an incarnation of the god Vishnu, resting on a cobra, the symbol of water.

The Middle Ages gave rise to a disc-like map of the world. The T that divided it into three continents represented the Mediterranean, river Don and the Red Sea. Jerusalem lay at the centre and the Garden of Eden was thought to be in Asia.

gaps between them. From the drift of these white wisps across the surface, a space observer could follow both the westward flow of the trade winds and the eastward procession of the major weather systems in the earth's middle latitudes. He would have to come fairly close to pick out the night-time glow of great cities, but even from a distance a good radio receiver would reveal that at least a portion of the inhabitants' multitude of electromagnetic signals penetrates the upper zones of the earth's atmospheric blanket and passes on into the space around it.

Other instruments would discern—as Explorer satellites initially disclosed to us—the vast, doughnut-shaped band of radiation that girdles the earth. First believed to consist of two bands and called the Van Allen belts, the zone was later renamed the magnetosphere. Up to 40,000 miles thick, it is a consequence of the earth's magnetic field, a trap imprisoning electrically charged particles from the sun and space.

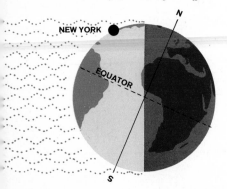

The seasons on earth are caused by the 23 1/2° tilt of its axis and its revolution around the sun. When the north pole of the axis is inclined away from the sun (above), winter comes to the Northern Hemisphere. The sun's rays strike a place like New York on a slant (below), their energy is less concentrated and the weather is consequently cold. The tilt shortens days, enhancing this effect.

FROM a vantage point in space, an observer could also watch the variety of motions in which the earth is endlessly engaged. The most obvious of these is the earth's daily rotation on its own axis. This is the motion responsible for the alternation of day and night, which occurs as each place on the earth faces towards and away from the sun. Less obviously, the earth also revolves around the sun once a year, in a 600-million-mile sweep that takes almost exactly $365\frac{1}{4}$ days and is responsible for the succession of the seasons. The orbit around the sun is not a perfect circle, but an ellipse: the earth's average 92.9-million-mile distance from the sun varies by 3,100,000 miles during the course of a year. The variation between winter and summer, contrary to the assumptions of some laymen, has very little to do with this alternate nearness to and distance from the sun. It is during the Northern Hemisphere's winter and Southern Hemisphere's summer, as it happens, that the earth comes closest to the sun.

What does account for the seasons is the tilt of the earth's axis. As the earth travels around the sun in its annual journey, the North Pole points towards the sun at the summer solstice, around the 21st June, but away from the sun at winter solstice, around the 22nd December (the angle of the tilt, relative to the plane of the earth's orbit, is $23\frac{1}{2}°$). The South Pole, of course, does exactly the opposite, which is why the seasons in the Southern Hemisphere are the reverse of those in the north. It is the angle at which the sun's rays strike the earth, rather than the distance they travel, that is critical in determining the earth's seasonal changes in temperature. A shaft of light that hits a surface at a right-angle delivers twice as much energy per square foot as does a shaft of light hitting at an angle of 30°. In either hemisphere, it is in summer that the sun's rays come closest to striking the surface at a right-angle, and in winter that they are the most oblique.

Far less apparent than the earth's tilt is the fact that the globe's elliptical path around the sun is not centred precisely in the centre of the earth. This is because, in its path around the sun, the earth-moon partnership, linked together by gravitation, behaves like a dumb-bell with a large ball at one end and a small one at the other. It is the centre of mass of this asymmetrical dumb-bell that actually traces the ellipse around the sun. Even though the earth is more than 80 times as heavy as the moon, the centre of mass of the earth-moon system still lies some 3,000 miles away from the exact centre of the earth. Thus, as the moon circles the earth each month, the centre of the earth traces an S-curve, with a range of almost 6,000 miles, along the path about the sun.

Superimposed upon this undulation in the earth's orbit are other, far subtler ones, also due to gravitational forces—in this case, the forces exerted by the other planets. However, these deviations are practically insignificant because, while all the planets are heavier than the moon—and most of them heavier by far—they are also much farther away.

Just as its orbital motion round the sun is imperfect, so the earth's rotation about its own axis is not altogether steady. Again, the main source of these irregularities is the moon. Its attraction for the earth's oceans causes the tides, and the weight of the tides slightly unbalances the earth's spin. At the same time, the moon's gravitational action on the earth's equatorial bulge, as the moon passes first south and then north of the equator, causes the earth's axis to wobble like an ill-spun top.

Long before men had measurements precise enough to detect the earth's equatorial bulge, this motion had been noted and measured. In 130 B.C. the Greek astronomer Hipparchus calculated that the sun completed its annual journey around the constellations of the Zodiac a little earlier each spring, reaching the point of vernal equinox a little farther to the east (about 50 seconds of arc) every year. This annual gain has been known ever since as the precession of the equinoxes. Despite the formality of the name "precession", this motion is none the less a commonplace movement, although so slow that it takes 25,800 years for the earth's axis to complete one. During this period the North and South Poles each trace out the base of a cone in space—with the apexes point-to-point at the earth's centre—and the "North Star" changes.

Some 5,000 years ago, Egyptian astronomer-priests found that the star that lay closest to true north was Alpha Draconis, not the star in the Little Bear's tail (Alpha Ursa Minoris, or Polaris) that serves as today's North Star. At present, the axial movement is slowly pointing the earth's North Pole ever closer towards Polaris, but in A.D. 2100 the pole will begin to diverge from the Little Bear until, in the year A.D. 14,000, the new North Star will be Vega. If any mariners ply the earth's seas 12 milleniums from now, they will have reason to be pleased with precession, for Vega is the brightest star in the northern sky. But by A.D. 28,000, when another cycle of precession is complete, Polaris will again take its turn as the North Star.

Summer comes to the Northern Hemisphere when the earth's axis tilts towards the sun (above). The day the axis is tilted closest to it is the summer solstice. On this day, in late June, New York gets 15 hours of daylight from concentrated, more nearly vertical solar rays. But in the Southern Hemisphere it is midwinter, and the sun shines only briefly and at a low angle on places like Buenos Aires.

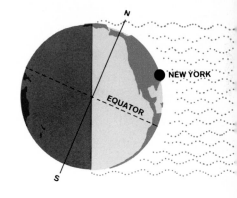

THE gravitational force of the sun also plays a part in precession, and sun and moon combine to produce still a sixth motion upon the earth. Because these paramount bodies constantly change their positions with respect to the earth, the forces they apply to produce precession are not at all constant. The result is a slight "nodding" of the earth's axis, called "nutation", that is superimposed on the slow motion of precession. This nodding movement is faster but less pronounced than precession: every 18.6 years—which is the length of a full cycle of the moon's own motions—the axis of the earth completes a "nod" that measures 9.2 seconds of arc—about 1/400th of a degree.

Such an array of undulations, nods, oscillations and whirlings might be deemed quite sufficient motions for any body. Yet the earth, as a member of the solar system, shares in two other motions as well. In the lesser of these, it follows the sun in that star's own 12-mile-per-second journey through our local star cloud in the general direction of the constellation Hercules. In the greater motion, the earth follows the sun in its major journey —a great, wheeling "annual" sweep around the hub of the Milky Way that takes 200 million years to complete—which is apparent as a seemingly straight-line motion, at a rate of 150 miles per second, towards the constellation Cygnus. Of a further, final motion shared by the earth—the motion of the Milky Way and its 2,500 neighbouring galaxies with respect to the thousands of millions of sister galaxy clusters that dot the universe—no sensible statement was possible until recently. In 1969 Edward K. Conklin of Kitt Peak National Observatory in Arizona measured this motion as well: 360,000 miles per hour in the direction of the Hunting Dogs constellation.

A VANTAGE point in near-by space would serve a Martian visitor another useful purpose: the unusual nature of the earth's influential neighbour, the moon, would be borne home. Other satellites among the solar system's vast, gassy outer planets rival and exceed our moon in size—Jupiter's Ganymede is three times as large—but no other body in the sun's entire family has proportionally so large a companion as does the earth. A mere frog's-jump distant from the earth by cosmic standards—at maximum distance the moon's centre is only a trifle over a quarter of a million miles from the earth's centre—the moon has a diameter that is more than a quarter that of the earth's, and more than two-thirds that of Mercury's. Indeed, modern thought on the formation of the solar system regards the moon as a legitimate planet, which either took shape as a near twin from the same cosmic raw material that the earth began with or, forming elsewhere in the same general zone, was captured later by the earth to make up the present double system.

It is impossible to consider the earth's history as a planet without giving due regard to what can be learned from a study of the moon. This lesser twin circles the earth in an elliptical orbit once each 27 1/3 days. With each such revolution, the moon also rotates on its axis exactly once, so that the earth's inhabitants never see the "back" of the moon. Actually, not only is the moon's axis inclined so that we alternately glimpse both its north polar and south polar regions, but both its shape and its motions are irregular enough for its swaying and nodding—called librations—to have permitted observatories on the earth to photograph 59 per cent of the moon's total surface. Brilliantly lit by the sun during the lunar day, the earthward face of the moon is dimly illuminated during the lunar night by sunlight reflected from the earth. An ideal subject for photography as well as visual observation, the moon's visible surface has been mapped in detail. Photographs of the far side, radioed back to earth by American and Russian space craft, showed it to be quite like the familiar near side.

The airless, waterless lunar landscape is dramatically marked by vast, dark plains (because of their resemblance to seas they were named *maria* by astronomers of the past), by jagged peaks that rival or surpass the greatest of the earth's mountains and by thousands of spectacular craters, as much as 180 miles across. In the absence of an appreciable atmosphere with its attendant water cycle, the sort of erosion that continually softens the earth's landscape is unknown to the moon. Its sharp-edged features know no buffing but the casual effects of meteorites and the savage wrench-

During a cycle of about 26,000 years, the axis of the earth, describing a cone around the ecliptic pole (perpendicular to the plane of the orbit), shifts enough to point from one North Star to several others. The star map above indicates how Alpha Draconis (A) was the North Star in 3000 B.C., and Polaris (B) is the North Star today. Alpha Cephei (C) will be in the year 7500, and Vega (D) in 14,000.

es of alternate expansion and contraction as the boiling heat of day—about 90° C.—is followed by a night chill that may drop to nearly 200° C. Even so, the testimony given by the Apollo astronauts, as well as the analyses of the rock specimens they brought home, reveal that the moon has not been exempt from wear and tear. When the early specimens arrived, in fact, lunar scientists were surprised not only by the variety of rocks but by the way they had apparently been subjected to churning and stirring over aeons of time. From tracks left in the rocks by bombarding cosmic-ray particles, it was easy to see that many of the rocks had been turned over several times, presumably by the impacts of meteorites. So violent have these impacts been that the lunar surface is sprinkled with rocks that have apparently come from places far away—perhaps hundreds of miles—from the spots where they were found.

What does the lunar landscape tell us about the earth's own past? Once it was believed that the vast array of craters on the moon represented a long succession of savage volcanic eruptions such as the earth has often known. Today, although scientists still debate the extent of volcanic action on the moon, they believe most of its surface scars are the result of ancient meteoritic bombardment. Following this clue in recent years, the nearly vanished traces of similar stupendous collisions on the earth have been detected. But much more remains to be learned about the nature of our own planet by studying the ceaseless bombardment of its surface by the chunks, lumps, fragments and specks of dust that continually rain down from the depths of space. But our knowledge of the moon poses other questions than those concerning landscape. From observations that yield the moon's dimensions and its mass, we know that the moon has an average density a full third less than the density of the earth. If both bodies were formed of much the same stuff, what accounts for this discrepancy? Because we can examine and weigh the various components of the earth's crust, we know that our planet's inner portions must be a great deal denser than its surface stuff in order to make the average density work out correctly. Although we know now the weight of moon dust and moon rock brought back by the astronauts, we still have very little idea how the densities of the moon's interior are apportioned.

Not long ago, it was believed that the brief flashes in the night sky that we know as meteor trails were somehow involved with the atmosphere and with the weather in general ("meteor" comes from the Greek for "high in the air"). There was logic in such a view, but it was based on the inaccurate assumption that lightning bolts—self-evidently mixed up with weather—produced something called thunderstones, actually odd rocks or, more often, the crude, unrecognized flint tools of early man. Meteor flashes, too, were sometimes accompanied by thunderous sounds and unidentifiable fragments of stone or iron. Although these occurrences were far rarer than electrical storms, it was hard to deny the obvious parallels of flashing light, noise and subsequent lump of matter. Not all meteor showers produce boloids—as the noisy, fragment-producing kind of meteorites are called—but then not all lightning is accompanied by thunder.

Even with today's understanding, the matter of meteors still involves complex language. Specialists are strict to distinguish between *meteoroids* (the bits of undefined matter, regardless of size or composition, that drift through space), *meteors* (the visible flashes of light produced by a meteoroid as it is heated to incandescence by its passage through the earth's atmosphere) and, finally, *meteorites* (the tangible fragments, ranging from dust to sizeable tonnages, that survive the fiery passage and reach the earth).

Meteorites are of three general classes: irons—composed of 98 per cent or more nickel-iron; stony irons—composed roughly of half nickel-iron and half of a kind of rock known as olivine; and, finally, stones. The stones are further subdivided, depending on whether they contain tiny bodies (or chondrules) of the minerals olivine and pyroxene. The stones that possess them—more than 90 per cent of all known meteoritic stones—are called chondrites. The few stones that lack these minerals are known as achondrites. All these categories offer useful clues to those who try to reconstruct the history of the earth, for not only are meteorites fellow members of the solar system, but radioactive dating indicates that they are as old as the earth itself.

Quite apart from a few spectacular falls that have brought irons weighing as much as 30 tons smashing into the earth, a vast amount of meteoritic dust continually falls from the heavens; estimates of the annual accumulation range from a few thousand to a few million tons. This dust consists of particles ranging from a ten-thousandth to a hundredth of an inch across. Meteoritic dust particles have been found around the world and may be extracted magnetically from rain-water collected at random. There is even a persuasive theory relating fluctuations in world-wide rainfall to fluctuations in the arrival of meteoritic dust.

UNFORTUNATELY the meteorites have little to tell about the meteoroids that are their presumed parents. Many meteor showers, for example, occur in streams with established orbits. (They are named after the constellation from which they appear to radiate: for example, the Perseids in early August and the Orionids in late October.) Some of these orbits are known to be the same as those of former comets—eccentric bodies that are normally the most outward inhabitants of the solar system. It is therefore plausible to suppose that all recurrent meteor showers represent the debris left in the wake of comets, past or present.

But the material of comets is notoriously insubstantial and it is doubtful if any "comet dust" ever reaches the earth's surface in the solid form of meteorites. Instead, it is the fall of sporadic meteorites that provides matter of particular interest to earth scientists. One popular theory holds that these fragments are debris left over from the disintegration of small planet-like bodies that had once been in orbit round the sun. The asteroid belt, lying generally between the orbits of Mars and Jupiter, could serve as an inexhaustible source of such fragments. The stony meteorites contain some minerals akin to those in the earth's crust. The crystalline structure displayed by meteoritic iron, in turn, could well have formed during the slow cooling of molten metal under immense pressure—a situation that is most easily imagined in the environment of a planet's interior. Finally, the stony irons could fit the theoretical half-metal, half-rock specification for some planetary layer between core and crust. The meteorites that have fallen and still fall to the earth—which in the past pockmarked the moon —offer tantalizing clues to the composition of those interior portions of our planet that lie always beyond reach, and clues to the earth's origin.

A MANY-HUED EARTH, PHOTOGRAPHED BY APOLLO 11 ASTRONAUTS FROM 112,000 MILES AWAY, SHIMMERS UNDER FLEECY CLOUDS.

The Earth in Space

We live in a celestial illusion. To all appearances, our earth hangs solidly in the heavens much as shown in the photograph above, while the rest of the universe wheels around it. Yet we know from the subtle proofs of science that this is not true. Our world, dragging its moon along, is awhirl in space. Its complex movements and some of their consequences are shown on the following pages.

WHIRLING, WOBBLING, NODDING, the earth exhibits the three basic motions shown in the painting above. Once each 24 hours, the earth rotates on its axis (*left*), spinning from west to east on its path around the sun. Once every 26,000 years, the tilted axis of the earth swings ponderous- ly around in a tight circle to trace a double conical figure (*centre*). This movement, called precession, is much like the wobbling of a top. The path of precession is not smooth since the gravitational pulls of the sun and moon create a slight back-and-forth nodding effect, or nutation (*right*).

Intricate Pathways in the Sky

The eight motions of the earth illustrated on these pages have been separated from each other for clarity. In space they go on simultaneously, one superimposed upon the other, following pathways of incredible complexity. (Try to move a finger as the earth's axis moves in these three drawings.) The intricate movements take place at fantastic speeds. A point on the earth's equator rotates at 1,050 miles an hour. The earth revolves around the sun at 1,100 miles a minute, and the sun moves through the galaxy at 150 miles a second. Only two of these motions have important direct effects on mankind. The rotation of the earth creates the cycle of night and day. And the revolution around the sun, taking just over 365 days, is the basis of our calendar and indirectly the cause of the changing seasons.

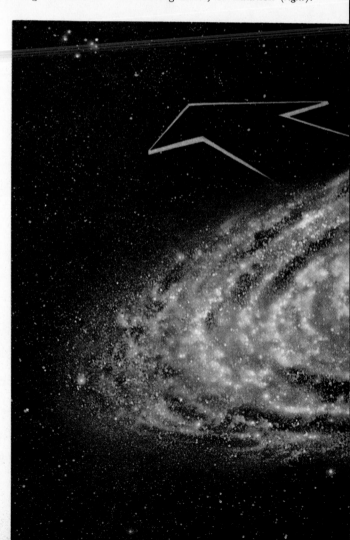

PLUNGING OUT into space with its galaxy (large arrow), the sun also circles among its neighbouring stars as indicated by the smaller arrow. The sum of these two motions is the spiral on the lower right.

IN ERRATIC REVOLUTION, the earth and moon trace an intertwined pattern in their yearly trip round the sun. The sun's gravity acts on the earth and moon as if they were coupled into a giant dumb-bell. It is the centre of the dumb-bell's mass, rather than the centre of the earth, which moves in a smooth ellipse (broken line). The centre of the earth follows a serpentine path (dotted line). The earth–moon system does not quite retrace its orbit in successive years. With each revolution, it begins a path in a position slightly counter-clockwise from the previous one (*lower right*).

GIRDLING THE WORLD in a tubular layer some 40,000 miles thick, the magnetosphere presents some risks to space travellers, but to mankind it is a reassuring sign that the earth is safe from bombardment by lethal radiation. Puffs of protons and electrons from the sun constantly bump into the earth's magnetic field. Most of this radiation is trapped in

A Magnetic Cage
of Captive Radiation

A critical and completely unexpected discovery about the earth in space astonished the scientific world in 1958. Dr. James Van Allen, head of a U.S. research team, announced that American Explorer and Pioneer satellites had found two great bands of radiation trapped high above the

the field, where it spirals to and fro along the lines of force without ever reaching Earth. Where it actually penetrates the atmosphere, near the magnetic poles, it agitates the air molecules to create the flaming auroras. Weak cosmic rays from space are mostly deflected by the magnetosphere, but the stronger ones flash relentlessly to the earth.

surface inside the earth's magnetic field. These were named the Van Allen belts. Subsequent satellite data have shown there are not two distinct belts, but one large one starting about 600 miles up and stopping rather abruptly at 40,000 miles. This band, called the magnetosphere, fans out into a thin tail of protons and electrons beyond the earth's dark side. Earlier fears of radiation danger to astronauts passing through the magnetosphere have been dispelled—traversing the region at the speeds used for trips to the moon and planets poses no serious hazard to space travellers.

The Fickle, Forceful Moon

The moon gives off no light of its own but only reflects the brilliance of the sun. As it moves in orbit round the earth, always showing only one side, the moon has phases in which it appears as a crescent, a half moon, a gibbous—or three-quarter—moon, and finally in its full glory (explanatory drawing below).

To the ancients, the changing moon appeared to be a living thing that grew in size, dwindled and died. It seemed reasonable that its waxing and waning could affect living things on earth. Seeds were sown when the moon was waxing, so that they would grow strong, and trees were felled in the waning moon when they were weakest.

Such lunar effects are now all but dismissed as superstition. But the moon does exert a strong influence on the earth. Although it is only 2,160 miles in diameter and one-eightieth the mass of the earth, it is so close (about 240,000 miles away) that its gravitational pull is felt strongly. The oceans are heaped into tides and even the land is affected. The North American continent may rise six inches when the moon is overhead.

THE MOON'S PHASES are caused by differences in the amount of its sunlit surface seen from the earth (outer circle). Actually, the moon is always half dark (inner circle), but the angle of view from the earth keeps changing (dotted lines), giving a "full" moon at A, a "new" moon at B.

A LUMINOUS BALL, the moon nearing full phase rises over a Bavarian lake (*opposite*). Even in the clearest weather the full moon is only 1/450,000th as bright as the midday sun.

A SILVER SLIVER, the crescent moon is seen in this multiple exposure as it descends over the Sahara north of Lake Chad. The white dot setting on the lower left is the planet Venus.

IN A LUNAR ECLIPSE, THE EARTH'S AMBER SHADOW CROSSES THE MOON'S FACE (LEFT AND CENTRE), NEARLY COVERING IT (RIGHT)

Eclipses: Shadows in the Sky

Eclipses are perhaps the most fearfully regarded of all natural phenomena. The dependable light of the sun or moon suddenly dims or fades out, leaving the creatures of earth uneasy in unaccustomed darkness. As seen in the diagram below, a solar eclipse occurs when the moon passes directly between the sun and the earth, while a lunar eclipse takes place when the moon passes through the earth's shadow. Such alignments in space are not especially rare. Each year, there are at least two eclipses of the sun and there may be as many as five, although most are partial eclipses in which

only a segment of the sun's face is covered. Lunar eclipses occur just as often and are seen over larger areas, although some are so faint that they can only be detected with instruments.

As a solar eclipse like the one opposite begins, a dark notch appears at the western edge of the sun, and the moon quickly bites its way deeper and deeper into the solar disc. As the face of the sun diminishes, a peculiar twilight rushes over the landscape. From start to finish an eclipse may last as much as four hours, but the dark climax seldom endures more than nine minutes.

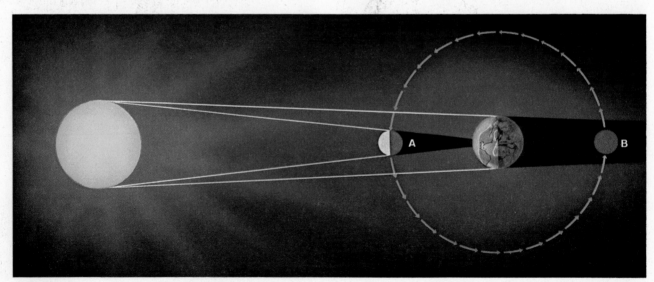

TWO KINDS OF ECLIPSES, solar and lunar, are shown above. When the moon is at position "A" in its orbit, the sun is eclipsed on those parts of the earth where the tip of the moon's conical shadow falls. When the moon is at position "B", it lies in the earth's shadow and a lunar eclipse occurs. In both cases all three bodies must be in line.

IN FIERY ECLIPSE, the sun's face is almost hidden by the dark disc of the moon. This is an annular eclipse, so called because a ring, or annulus, of sunlight is still visible around the moon's edge. In a total eclipse, when the moon is closer to the earth, the entire sun is obscured. This picture was taken in the North African desert in December 1955.

AN OBLIQUE MOONSCAPE OF AN AREA ABOUT AS BIG AS MASSACHUSETTS, CONNECTICUT AND RHODE ISLAND REVEALS VOLCANIC DOMES

Two Views of the Bleak Lunar Landscape

To earth-bound viewers the most striking features on the moon's surface are its craters. More than 30,000 craters, from 1 mile to 180 miles in diameter, have been charted by telescope. But until they were studied at close range by satellites, their origins remained a mystery. Did they result from meteoritic bombardment or from volcanic activity? The historic photograph above, made by Lunar Orbiter II late in 1966 of the Marius Hills region on the moon, was the first proof that both forces had played a part in shaping the 4,500 mil-

lion-year-old lunar landscape. Seen in detail for the first time was an array of irregularly shaped lunar domes, somewhat like those found in the north-western U.S., which had undoubtedly been formed by the upwelling of molten rock from the moon's interior. This evidence, supported by instrument tests and by analyses of the rocks brought back by the astronauts, suggests a volcanic origin not only for the domes but for some of the smaller craters. But the largest craters are undoubtedly the result of meteor bombardment.

FROM 2 TO 10 MILES DIAMETER AND ABOUT 1,500 FEET HIGH. AT THE UPPER RIGHT IS THE IMPACT CRATER MARIUS, 25 MILES WIDE AND 1 MILE DEEP

ON THE MOON'S SURFACE, a close-up made by astronaut Neil Armstrong shows the pebbly lunar soil and, in the background, a small crater. A stereo-camera is visible in the lower left corner.

27

Mapping the Moon

Squinting with naked eye, peering through telescopes, studying pictures televised from satellites brought back by astronauts, generations of astronomers have been compiling an atlas of the moon. The side of the moon that always faces the earth was mapped long ago. Because the moon nods and sways slightly in its orbit around the earth, it was possible to chart somewhat more than half of its total surface. Principal features are usually given Latin appellations or named after scientists or philosophers. In the 1960s, with the advent of space vehicles that could fly round the moon, the previously hidden side of the moon was revealed in photographs like those at the right. And with the first lunar landings in 1969, close-up pictures told much more about areas known earlier.

FAMILIAR SIDE OF THE MOON, PHOTOGRAPHED IN SHARP DETAIL, SHOWS PEAKS AND CRATERS AS SMALL AS A QUARTER OF A MILE ACROSS.

A WIDE-ANGLE VIEW of the southern hemisphere of the far side of the moon was taken by Orbiter II's television camera and then beamed back to earth. The picture reveals topography identical with that on the familiar side.

THIS ORBITER 1 PHOTOGRAPH SHOWS HOW CLOUD-BOUND EARTH LOOKS TO AN ASTRONAUT ORBITING ROUND THE MOON'S FAR SIDE

The Mysterious Meteorites

Meteorites were the earth's only tangible samples of matter from space until the first spacemen brought back rocks and dust from the moon. Many meteorites are fragments of asteroids that collided with one another, although some may be "planetesimals" left over from the clouds of cosmic dust out of which our solar system grew. Most of these fragments that come within the earth's gravitational pull and fall through the atmosphere are made of stone. The largest meteorites, however, like the one below, are metallic, consisting mostly of dense nickel-iron alloys. The largest ever discovered is estimated to weigh 62 tons. Only two to eight meteorite falls of appreciable size occur each year in an area as large as the United States, but there is a constant rain of space dust, which filters down at the rate of perhaps a million tons a year.

PUZZLING PARTICLES of glassy matter, the meteorites called tektites may have come from ancient asteroid explosions.

THE LARGEST METEORITE ever recovered in the United States is the Willamette, found near Portland, Oregon, in 1902. It is a conical mass of nickel-iron and weighs 12 tons.

A TOUGH IRON METEORITE wore out a stack of 82 band-saw blades (*opposite*) when scientists cut it in half to see the effects of its blazing plunge through the earth's atmosphere.

THREE TYPES OF METEORITES show different structures. On the left is an iron meteorite, cut, polished and etched with acid to reveal the pattern of its nickel-iron alloys. In the centre is a stony meteorite section with a grainy texture similar to terrestrial rock. On the right is a stony-iron, its network of nickel-iron alloy filled with a stone called "olivine".

Missiles from Outer Space

Few large meteorites strike the earth. Most burn up in the atmosphere, or explode and reach the ground as fine dust. It is fortunate that they do, for when a large meteorite survives its fiery flight and hits the earth, it can do tremendous damage. A giant meteorite hit the Arizona desert in prehistoric times and dug a crater 4,100 feet across and 600 feet deep (*below*). A more puzzling cataclysm from space occurred in northern Siberia in 1908. There an explosion flattened the surrounding forest for a distance of 40 miles (*opposite*). It was long thought to be a meteorite blast, but Soviet scientists now believe it was caused by a comet—a mass of frozen gases—colliding with the earth.

AN UNLUCKY TARGET of a meteorite, Mrs. Hewlett Hodges was bruised by a 10-pound fragment that pierced the roof of her house (*top picture*) and struck her left side.

CANYON DIABLO CRATER NEAR WINSLOW, ARIZONA, WAS BLASTED

A FLATTENED FOREST in Siberia, long thought to have been hit by a meteor in 1908, is now believed to have been the work of a comet which exploded just before reaching the ground. A "ball of fire" crossed the sky, followed by a tremendous blast. Men and animals 100 miles away were bowled over, and pressure waves were recorded in London.

OUT WHEN AN IRON METEORITE OF OVER 13,000 TONS PLUNGED TO EARTH AND EXPLODED, SCATTERING MILLIONS OF FRAGMENTS

2

Cloudy Beginnings

WHILE knowledge of the earth's size and shape is as old as Greek geometry and as modern as Cape Kennedy's rockets, man's understanding of the planet's origin—and its exact composition—is notoriously imprecise. "In the beginning . . . the earth was without form, and void", *Genesis* announces with unimprovable terseness—but when *was* the beginning? It is unlikely that even Archbishop James Ussher, if he had it to do over again, would date creation today as unequivocally (or as recently) as he did in 1650 when he pin-pointed it at the stroke of 9 a.m. on Sunday, the 23rd October, 4004 B.C. Once it was dignified as a marginal note in the King James version of the Bible, his date stood for nearly three centuries as an all but ineradicable bench-mark of fundamentalist chronology.

Yet the earth certainly has not existed always. If it were eternally old, the various radioactive elements still in its crust would have decayed into different, inert elements long ago. The earth is old indeed—today most geologists accept a figure of 4,500 million years—but at one time there was no earth, and the circumstances of its birth present one of the most fascinating riddles still before science.

There has been no lack of valiantly attempted solutions and imaginative theories. Some ancient mythologies pictured the nascent earth as a warm body of liquid. The philosopher Descartes, in 1644, saw it as a sun-like incandescent body. In the 18th century the German philosopher Immanuel Kant and the French astronomer, the Marquis de Laplace, thought it condensed out of a gaseous nebula surrounding the sun. Various later hypotheses—now mostly considered to be untenable—have described the earth as a child of the sun, either blasted out of it by some internal explosion or torn away from it by the force of a collision, or near-collision, with some wayward passing star. The whole tantalizing question of the earth's chemical and physical evolution is, of course, inescapably linked to the larger questions of the origin of the solar system, of stars in general, of galaxies—and of the entire universe.

As to even the first of these questions, however—the creation of the solar system—a contemporary American astronomer, Gerard P. Kuiper, has pointed out that all possible theories involve assumptions that are simply beyond man's power to verify. "It is not a foregone conclusion", says Kuiper, ". . . that the problem has a scientific solution. For instance, an enclosure in which the air has been stirred gives, after some delay, no clue to the nature or the time of the stirring. All memory of the event within the system has been lost."

BODE'S LAW

One of the most productive and puzzling laws of science was published by the German astronomer Johann Bode in the 1770s. Bode noted that the distances of the various planets from the sun fell into a curious mathematical sequence. He published a paper which arbitrarily assigned numbers to the planets: 0, 3, 6, 12, 24, 48, 96, 192. Thus Mercury was numbered 0, Venus 3, Earth 6, Mars 12, and so on, each number being double the last one.
● When 4 was added to each of these numbers and the result divided by 10, figures emerged which almost exactly equalled the planets' distances from the sun, measured in astronomical units. (An astronomical unit is the distance from the earth to the sun: 93 million miles.)
● The table on the opposite page shows how Bode's calculations work out, compared to the true distances as measured by modern scientific methods.
● The only trouble with the law was that there were no planets at positions 24 or 192. But astronomers, searching in position 24, located the asteroids. Uranus, which was discovered in 1781, occurs at position 192 and conforms almost exactly with Bode's calculations. Only the outermost planets, Neptune and Pluto (illustrated below), fail to obey the law.
● Today, many astronomers dismiss Bode's law as a coincidence. Yet it remains one of the most mysterious statements of natural law formulated by man.

With this warning, what can be said about the earth's first, embryonic days? Many astronomers now agree on a probable chain of events occurring inside an interstellar cloud of gases and dust that measured as far across as the entire solar system does today. For a long time this dust cloud may have been formless, but at some point the force of gravity working within the cloud caused it to collapse into a flattened, revolving disc. In the course of 80 million years or so this disc sorted itself into a dense contracting centre and a series of surrounding concentric rings. The centre, amounting to almost 90 per cent of the mass of the original dust cloud, was the protosun, huge, cool, and therefore not yet incandescent. The rings, containing the remaining 10 per cent of the original aggregate of gas and dust, were the cloudy stuff from which protoplanets would form. Each ring was destined for a distinctive character as a planet, depending on its distance from the central mass and the exact nature of its raw materials.

Proto-earth was a special case in the array of spinning rings. As noted in the first chapter, the earth and its moon are unique in the solar system, for no other planet has a companion proportionately as large. So within the dust-cloud hypothesis, two possibilities exist to explain the formation of the moon: either proto-earth developed two increasingly dense nuclei, which grew as a pair, or else two quite separate protoplanets developed from adja-

MERCURY   VENUS   EARTH   MARS   ASTEROIDS   JUPITER   SATURN cent rings of raw material, and later captured each other in a near-collision.

Whichever the case, proto-earth was probably 500 times heavier and 2,000 times its present diameter, just as all the protoplanets were far larger than the bodies they evolved into. Over the millions of years their heavier elements sank inwards to form massive cores enveloped by lighter gases, mostly hydrogen and helium. Meanwhile their sun was contracting too. In due time it reached a critical density where nuclear reactions in its interior began to evolve heat.

Up to this point the whole process has taken place in virtual darkness. But now the sun began to shine and to evaporate streams of ions from its surface. These hot streams swept the nearer planets free of the gases that still clung to them. The planets themselves grew warm, and the blowing away of gas was enhanced by evaporation. After some hundreds of millions of years, with most of their mass boiled away by solar radiation, what remained was the sun-warmed, shrunken, virtually naked inner planets and the gas-enveloped outer planets of the present day.

The whole leisurely sequence is reasonably consistent with what is known about the existing solar system. All the planetary orbits except that of Pluto lie within a few degrees of the sun's equatorial plane, and Pluto's is only 17° away from that plane. (Pluto may not even have been a real planet originally, but an escaped moon of Neptune.) The planets all revolve about the sun and rotate on their own axes; all except Venus rotate in the same direction as the sun—counter-clockwise as seen from over its north pole—though for some reason a few of the satellites turn clockwise. The planets' distances from the sun fall into the most remarkable regularity. Further, their combined rotational momentum, which is 49 times that of the sun, squares with the theory. If they had been born in some solar catastrophe, the sun's rotational momentum, as well as its bulk, would dwarf theirs.

What is known of the earth's own structure also fits in plausibly. When the dense core of proto-earth came into being, the shrinking process itself, as well as the heat-yielding radioactive elements present, began to raise the temperature of the whole mass. Eventually the earth became molten, but as the energy of contraction was exhausted and the initial radioactive content decayed, it began to cool down, a process that may or may not still be going on.

UNTIL the earth could be weighed, speculation about its anatomy could be no better informed than the early theories about its origin. Various natural philosophers had offered a variety of proposals: an earth filled with water (its cataclysmic outburst, in early times, causing the Flood); an earth whose crust was dust, floating on a supporting bath of oil; even a hollow earth, with cavities alternately full of fire or water. All these geogonies,

THE PLANET'S POSITIONS

PLANET	BODE'S PREDICTED DISTANCE	ACTUAL DISTANCE
Mercury	0.4	0.39
Venus	0.7	0.72
Earth	1.0	1.00
Mars	1.6	1.52
Asteroids	2.8	2.65
Jupiter	5.2	5.20
Saturn	10.0	9.50
Uranus	19.6	19.20
Neptune	38.8	30.10
Pluto	77.2	39.50

(Figures are in astronomical units. One unit equals 93 million miles.)

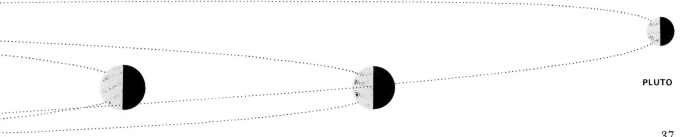

URANUS   NEPTUNE   PLUTO

as they were called, necessarily vanished in 1798 when the English physicist, Henry Cavendish, "weighed" the earth. His starting-point was Newton's law of universal gravitation, which holds that every body in the universe attracts every other body with a force directly proportional to both their masses and inversely proportional to the square of the distance between them. Cavendish built a yard-long dumb-bell, hung it from a thread, measured the attraction between its twin balls and two larger spheres, calculated the gravitational constant—and from this, together with such known quantities as the earth's diameter, derived a weight of six thousand trillion (6×10^{21}) tons. As estimates go in problems of such magnitude, it was and is a good one.

For its volume, which is about 260 thousand million cubic miles, the earth is the heaviest planet in the solar system. Its average density is five and a half times that of water. (Saturn, at the other extreme, is so light that it would float in water.) But the average density of the rocks that make up the earth's crust—light granites and dense basalts together—is only a fraction more than half the density of the earth as a whole. To the scientists who first pondered this, one fact was immediately clear: the density of whatever composes the earth's interior had to be far greater than that of the surface rocks. The earth neither had room for such "lightweights" as fire and water inside, nor was it like a giant Edam cheese, a great ball made of the same stuff all the way through.

Such an insight seems elementary today. But at the start of the 19th century, when geology began to outgrow its prolonged infancy, facts of this kind were invaluable stepping-stones. Even today, every idea about the interior of the earth is conjecture—but it is conjecture based on a foundation of ingenious conclusions, largely drawn from observation of the natural disasters known as earthquakes.

ALTHOUGH only about a score of severe earthquakes wrench the earth on average in the course of a year, there are approximately a million minor tremors during the same period, or about two a minute. They provide a continuous source of data for analysis of the earth's interior. As a result of a century of such study, seismologists know that nearly all the major earthquakes originate in two long, relatively narrow zones. The principal zone is a belt in the lands that border the Pacific Ocean, running up the west coast of North and South America, and down the coast of Asia. The second major zone runs from west to east across Europe and Asia, from Spain and northern Africa through Italy, Greece, Turkey, India and Burma, to join the Pacific belt at Celebes. The first zone, known as the Pacific "ring of fire" because of the presence of most of the world's volcanoes along its path, is also the site of more than 80 per cent of all earthquakes, while the second zone is responsible for an additional 15 per cent or so. The remaining earthquakes occur at scattered positions elsewhere on the earth.

Nearly all earthquakes originate in fractures of the solid rock of the earth's crust along one zone or another. These fractures, called faults, occur when stresses that develop within the earth become too great for the brittle crust to bear. A spectacular example is the San Andreas fault in California. The land mass east of the San Andreas fault is steadily inching its way south, and every so often the motion goes beyond the stretching ability of the underlying rock. When this happens, the rock ruptures. On the 18th April, 1906, the ground shifted as much as 15½ feet along 200-odd miles of the San Andreas fault, causing an earthquake that demolished much of San Francisco. It was the most extensive earth shift ever recorded for a single quake. The movement along Pacific Coast faults also shook California in 1857, 1922 and 1940. We know that others can be expected. For earthquakes are now recognized as the inevitable creaks and groans of the jerkily moving machine called earth. They suggest how tenuous is our foothold on this globe.

A MAJOR earthquake is one of nature's most awesome events. In violence it may exceed the detonation of a thousand million tons of TNT, and while the most severe disturbance is localized, the shock may convulse wide areas. The Lisbon earthquake of 1755, for example, not only wrecked the heart of that city and killed thousands of its people, but also made itself felt over a million and a half square miles of Europe. All over the Continent the waters of lakes and rivers were violently disturbed, and sea waves from the quake rushed all the way across the Atlantic to the West Indies in a few hours. The quake occurred on the 1st November—All Saints' Day—when the faithful all over Europe were in church. In the great cathedrals, awed spectators watched the chandeliers shake and swing to the shock waves from Lisbon.

The Lisbon quake was not the first, by any means, to have alarmed Europeans. But it was the most destructive by far, and the scale of the disaster reminded scientists how little they knew about the nature of earth tremors. One of them, the English astronomer-mathematician John Michell, collected all the reports he could find and was able to calculate that the shock wave had travelled at a speed of more than 20 miles a minute. Michell prophetically guessed that the source of the shock was an earth movement deep in the crust: ". . . it could not be much less than a mile or a mile and a half [deep]," he wrote, "and . . . it is probable that it did not exceed three miles."

Less than 30 years after the Lisbon disaster, a series of severe earthquakes convulsed the Calabrian district of Italy, taking a toll of 35,000 lives. This second disaster, as well as Michell's inspiration concerning the great depths —far below the reaches of the deepest mine—at which the destructive shocks were born, served to bring more and more scientific effort to bear on the earthquake question. An urgent need was felt for some instrument that would measure the upheavals. Purely subjective reporting developed a rough scale of earthquake intensity, ranging in steps from slight to catastrophic. Later it became known that the shock waves at an earthquake's centre produce an up-and-down motion and that, as they travel outwards like ripples in a pond, these waves gradually become more horizontal. But there were no clues as to the direction from which distant shocks came, and the speed of travel, while realized to be rapid, was not known with any precision. It seemed possible that some new appparatus would not only supply this missing information but also, because of the depth at which earthquakes evidently begin, provide vital information about the earth's unknown interior.

Despite these incentives it was not until 1855—a century after the Lisbon tragedy—that the first seismograph was constructed. Today hundreds of these instruments, with a variety of refinements, are at work in seismological laboratories around the world. No single seismograph can disclose the point

A seismograph, shown in this simplified drawing, records an earthquake in the following way: the two metal frames, anchored in rock, pick up earth vibrations. A heavy pendulum, suspended from one of the frames by a wire coil to keep it static, traces the movements of the other frame and its rotating drum on the unfurling graph paper—thus giving an accurate measure of the earthquake's force.

at which an earthquake's tremors start. All, however, can show how far away an earthquake is.

Basically, a seismological station has three seismographs, one mounted vertically, and two mounted horizontally at right-angles so that one instrument will react to waves that pass to the north or south, while the other responds to waves from east or west. In essence, each seismograph consists of a support, firmly anchored to bedrock, and a heavy weight that hangs freely suspended from the support by a spring. As an earth tremor shakes the support, the flexible spring keeps these bedrock motions from reaching the suspended weight, which tends to hold its original position. In the process, the spring stretches or contracts and these changes in the spring are recorded. The combined seismographic records from three different places can narrow the possible sources of incoming waves to two spots on earth, only one of which is likely to be in an earthquake zone.

One of the first fruits of this new instrument was the realization that an earthquake's shock is transmitted in several different forms. The slowest is called a surface wave, which travels like an ocean wave along the curve of the earth's thin crust. Other waves, unsuspected before seismographs revealed them, drive, instead, straight into the body of the earth at a speed substantially greater than that of the surface waves. They proved to be of two kinds, primary—or P—and secondary—or S—waves. Of this speedy pair, P waves are the faster and more penetrating, moving without hindrance through the dense matter of the earth's interior. The slower S waves have a transverse movement—most commonly seen when a taut cord is plucked, or when a whip is cracked. A fact of significance, as will be shown, is that transverse waves travel well enough through solids, but disappear when they encounter liquids or gases.

At any seismograph station, the first sign that an earthquake has occurred is the arrival of a train of P waves—the fastest ones. Later—the interval depending on the distance to the station from the earthquake's focus—the S waves arrive. Still later, the slower surface waves, journeying along the thin, curved medium of the earth's crust, make their distinctive squiggle on the seismograph's revolving drum. (In some cases, seismographs can also point to the source, and indicate the force, of a volcanic eruption—or of a nuclear explosion.)

So far as exploring the earth's interior is concerned, the most useful facts that seismographs provide are the travel times of earthquake waves from their centres to the seismological observatories that dot the earth. From a sufficiently complete set of travel times, it is possible to infer the speeds of P and S waves at various depths in the earth. It has been found, for example, that these speeds tend to increase gradually as the waves pass nearer the earth's centre. There are also several precisely defined depths at which sudden shifts in the speed of travel occur. Such shifts must signify radical changes in the properties of the earth's interior matter, and the boundaries they mark between concentric layers of chemically or physically different kinds of material are therefore known as discontinuities.

The uppermost of the discontinuities is named after its discoverer, Andrija Mohorovičić. Above the Mohorovičić discontinuity there lies only the crust of the earth, a thin shell of rock about three miles thick under the sediments that coat the ocean floors, but with an average thickness of some 20

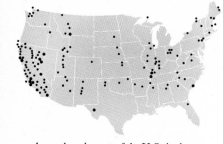

An earthquake map of the U.S.A. shows that tremors have occurred in nearly all parts of the country. The most serious quakes (large dots) and the greatest number occur in California, but many have also taken place in Montana and Utah.

miles under the continents. This crust seems to have two chief components: a three-mile-thick layer of heavy basalt that surrounds the entire earth, and blocks of lighter granite rock, as much as 40 miles thick, superimposed on the basalt to form the continents.

At the Mohorovičić discontinuity, the P and S waves accelerate from 4.3 and 2.4 miles per second respectively to 5 and 2.9 miles per second. Their rate of travel then increases steadily for the next 1,800 miles downwards until they reach speeds of 8.5 and 4.5 miles per second respectively. At this depth the speed of P waves suddenly drops to 5 miles per second and their direction of travel changes sharply, while the S waves disappear. Evidently a dramatic change in the earth's interior takes place at this 1,800-mile-deep boundary between the earth's mantle and its core.

Below the 1,800-mile-deep discontinuity lies the earth's core. Much indirect evidence supports the notion that at this depth the core is composed of molten iron, perhaps with some nickel and a trace of cobalt. First, the core must be very dense, to help to account for the earth's great weight. This points to iron as the chief ingredient of the 42,000 million cubic miles of core, for iron is the only heavy element relatively abundant throughout the universe. Moreover, at the estimated pressures and temperatures of the earth's core, iron would have a density—at least 588 pounds per cubic foot—that fits the weight requirements and it would also be a liquid. That the earth's core *is* liquid may be inferred from seismograph data revealing the inability of earthquake S waves to pass through it (their transverse vibrations can travel only through solids).

On the basis of further seismographic studies, some geophysicists think that still another major discontinuity exists—this one situated about 800 miles from the centre of the earth and indicating another, different region *within* the core. Thus, working from the earth's surface downwards, there would be a crust (a few miles), mantle (1,800 miles), outer core (1,375 miles) and inner core (800 miles). The difference between the inner and outer cores could be a chemical one—perhaps a slightly altered alloy of iron with nickel—or simply physical: perhaps the inner core is solid rather than liquid. Refined measuring systems in the future may permit better informed guesses but direct knowledge of the earth's core lies farther beyond man's reach than outer space.

The mantle, relatively close to the surface, contains over 80 per cent of the earth's volume as compared with the crust's $1\frac{1}{2}$ per cent. At present it is possible only to guess at the nature of this region. Some geophysicists surmise that much—perhaps most—of the mantle is composed of various types of dunite, a rock with properties that seem to fit in well with what little is understood about this vast region. Seen on the earth's surface, dunite is a green or rust-coloured, coarse-grained rock. But the mantle may also contain peridotite, a greenish-brown rock, in some regions, and eclogite, a pale pink similar rock, in others.

The crust is the part of the earth's structure we can reach and study. It is virtually all solid rock. This is not immediately apparent, for sediments cover the ocean floor and, above water, soil, vegetation and rock fragments such as sand and gravel are littered everywhere. But this cloak of crustal debris occurs in superficial layers measurable in feet or yards, while the thickness of the underlying bedrock is measured in miles. Furthermore, the rocks at the surface of the earth's crust are much the same as those deeper down, right to the level of the mantle. Mine and well shafts, the deepest of which descend as far as five miles, go through the same stuff all the way down. Similarly, volcanic rock shows no great differences whether it has risen in molten form from chambers just a few miles below ground or from depths as great as 100 miles in the mantle.

Rocks have been classified and subclassified almost endlessly by zealous petrographers but all belong to three great groups: the igneous, the sedimentary and the metamorphic. All igneous rocks were once molten and are believed to have come from deep in the earth, cooling at various rates and assuming various forms ranging from smooth basalt to grainy granite. Sedimentary rocks, as their name implies, are formed of layers of such materials as sand and clay washed down into lake beds and ocean floors. Those sediments may be laid down by water, by ice or by wind. Cemented under pressure and often raised up again by later earth movements, they include the familiar sandstones and shales, limestones and dolomites. It is in these rocks, particularly in shales and limestones, that fossil deposits are found. The metamorphic rocks are also aptly named: they are changed in form, reborn by heat and pressure during periods of deep burial. Thus slate was once clay, quartzite is a changed form of sandstone, and marble is reconstituted limestone. Geologists are not unanimously agreed on these groupings. For example, some of them believe that most granite is metamorphic rather than igneous in origin.

However formed, rocks are complex mixtures of various elements in the form of mineral compounds. Of the 92 natural elements known on the earth, only eight are commonly involved in rock formation; they constitute 98 per cent of the earth's crust by weight. The most abundant element in the crust—47 per cent of it—is oxygen. Silicon is next, at 28 per cent. From there the percentages drop sharply: aluminium totals 8 per cent, iron 5 per cent, and sodium, magnesium, potassium and calcium less than 4 per cent each. These eight common elements, together with several not so common ones, combine chemically in simple or complicated ways to form nearly 2,000 known minerals. But it is hardly surprising that in terms of volume oxygen-silicon compounds predominate and that only a dozen or so mineral compounds account for the bulk of the earth's crust.

M AN's only direct experience with rock formation comes from what he has seen of active volcanoes—orifices in the earth's crust from which molten rock, hot enough to flow like incandescent toffee, pours forth. This is the prototype of all igneous rocks. Such molten stuff is called magma when underground and lava when it emerges, and the nature of a volcanic eruption depends upon the rock's composition and content of gas and water. A viscous magma, laden with gas, tends to escape explosively, spewing fragments of solidified lava and billowing clouds of steam and hot gases. A thinner magma, with a smaller gas content, pushes out in quieter fashion, forming tongues of white-hot lava that creep downhill and harden.

The giant volcanoes that have formed the Hawaiian Islands rear as high as 30,000 feet above the ocean floor, 14,000 feet or so of this eminence being above sea level. Lava from the active volcanoes of Hawaii often emerges as an incandescent, highly fluid stream, sometimes spurting up in transient fountains when a pocket of gas comes to the surface. Such flows

Pin-pointing of an earthquake's place of origin, or epicentre, is done by three or more seismic stations in different cities. Each determines the interval between the arrival of the fast primary waves and the slower secondary waves, and from this time span estimates the distance they travelled. Three circles with radii representing these distances are drawn on a map. At their intersection is the epicentre (E).

may travel for long distances before solidifying; characteristically, they produce wide-based mountains. At the other extreme are volcanoes with thick lavas, which build up steep, narrow cones.

Magma does not always reach the surface by the volcanic route. In fact it sometimes does not reach the surface at all. If it can find no outlet or if there is not sufficient pressure behind it to force one, it may merely thrust its way up into cracks or between layers of rock near the surface. Sometimes it forms underground lakes, pushing up the surface above like a blister but not breaking through. Often it runs along natural fissures, occasionally engulfing and melting what lies in its path. Magma that has worked its way into a vertical crack and hardened there like a wall is called a dike. Dikes vary in width from a few inches to several yards and may be many miles in length. They may be revealed millions of years after their formation when the softer rock around them has been eroded away, leaving the dikes, exposed to the elements, running like long fences across the surface of the land. A few are immense. One in Rhodesia is 300 miles long and up to five miles wide.

A horizontal sheet of solidified underground magma is known as a sill. The magnificent Palisades that line the bank of the river Hudson opposite New York City are, in reality, a tremendous sill. Their appearance is deceptive; they look like a series of immense crumbling stone columns. But these columns are only one edge of the sill and their vertical appearance derives from the shrinkage of the original magma as it solidified.

Sills are dwarfed by the most gigantic of all molten rock formations. These are batholiths, enormous bodies of granitic rock that may be tens of thousands of square miles in area, extending downwards to unknown depths. What causes batholiths is a subject of controversy. Some geologists think that the magma has simply forced its way into older rock formations on a huge scale, pushing them upwards and aside as it rose towards the surface. Others think that the intense heat generated by a large amount of magma enables it to swallow up and melt the rocks above it, thereby growing in volume at the expense of existing rocks rather than forcing them aside. A third school holds that batholiths were never magma—that they are not of igneous origin at all but are metamorphic. This school contends that no lava field, above or below the surface, could be as large as some batholiths and that only the exertion of subterranean heat and pressure on a grand scale can yield such masses of homogeneous material.

THE texture and appearance of magma varies enormously according to whether it has been cooled rapidly on the surface of the earth in the form of lava or whether it has remained underground in batholiths and cooled very slowly. The rapid cooling of lava gives it a fine-grained character ranging all the way from obsidian, which is the most quickly cooled of all lava and looks like blackish glass, to basalt, a smooth, dark, dense material that is the most common of all volcanic rocks. By contrast, subsurface magma cools so very slowly that its structure is much coarser. A typical dike or batholith is made of granite, which is a grainy rock, speckled in colour and full of relatively large particles of different minerals.

From the granite of a surface dike to the inner core there is a dramatic increase in density. This is probably only partly a consequence of differences in composition. The steady increase in pressure at increasing depths within the earth also squeezes atoms together to form denser materials. The over-burden of crust and mantle, for example, weighs down on the sphere of the earth's outer core with a pressure of about 10,000 tons per square inch, while the incredibly compressed cubic inch of matter at the earth's exact centre is supporting nearly 20,000 tons of pressure on each of its six faces.

With such increases in pressure it is logical to expect increases in temperature and, even by the 17th century, miners at work in deep, dry shafts in Germany had reported steady rises in temperature with increasing depth. For those shallow portions of the earth's crust that man has so far probed, this increase in heat is at the rate of 1° C. for each 100 feet of depth. If this rate of increase held good all the way to the centre of the earth, the core's heart would be a hell-fire of 200,000° C.—or 35 times as hot as the surface of the sun.

No geophysicists are prepared to believe this; estimates of the core's maximum temperature vary between 2,000° C. and 4,500° C., compared to the sun's estimated surface temperature of 5,500° C. Such temperatures are above the normal melting point of any substance. Yet, with a few exceptions, most of the earth's interior is probably not fluid but rather squeezed into a hard solid by pressure. In any case, the present temperature distribution within the earth—whatever it may be—is not permanent. Both the mantle and the core surely hold a substantial residue of radioactive isotopes of uranium, thorium and potassium that release heat as they decay. And many geophysicists believe that the earth's interior temperature is gradually rising. This is nothing to worry about: both the mantle and the crust are superlative insulators and it will take millions of years for temperature changes within the body of the earth to be felt on the surface. Surface temperatures are almost entirely controlled by the sun; its effect is thousands of times as great as that of the heat flow from within the earth.

THAT man will ever penetrate the planet's core is unlikely except in science fiction; but that he will send instruments through the crust and into the mantle is inevitable. Indeed, both Russians and Americans have made a series of probes. Taking advantage of the fact that the earth's crust is thinnest under the ocean floor, the U.S. Project Mohole—a title derived from the name of the crust-and-mantle boundary—began in 1961 to sink test drillings as deep as 1,035 feet below the floor. Subsequent borings, the Russians working on land and the Americans at sea, went even farther.

Drilling into the earth's mantle has been called "man's greatest geological project". But the costs will be high: when Project Mohole was cancelled in 1966 some £20 million had already been spent or committed. The benefits of exploration, however, are many. In addition to considerable industrial and technological advances—oil, mineral and chemical resources previously locked from man's grasp will come within reach—scientific knowledge can be immeasurably enriched. From continuous core samples of the sediments, rocks and fossils in the earth's crust will come evidence of the origins and history of this planet, of others in the solar system and of life itself. Already deep-sea drillings have brought much new knowledge about the theory of continental drift and the mechanism of earthquakes.

As subsequent chapters will reveal, our life is profoundly influenced by the deep subterranean fires of the earth, for according to new theories these fires drive the mechanism that is still at work shaping our earth.

THE PLANETS FORM ROUND THE SUN OUT OF GAS AND SWIRLS OF DUST. PROTO-EARTH AND MOON ARE ON THE RIGHT IN THIS PAINTING

The Unquiet Planet

Ever since the earth first took tentative shape in the blackness of space, immense forces have been at work on it, from the outside and from within. What goes on in its interior is no longer as unfathomable as it once was: from clues provided by earthquakes and eruptions, man is beginning to understand the mysterious stirrings of his planet.

The Fires within the Globe

Our earth, once so cold, long ago warmed up, on the inside, to temperatures between 2,000° and 4,500° C. Thanks to the insulation of the earth's mantle and crust, little of the interior heat ever manifests itself on the surface. But hot springs and geysers, in a minor way, and volcanoes, in a spectacular way, give evidence of the searing heat that prevails far below. Volcanoes are fired by the same nuclear and frictional forces that maintain this locked-in heat. Their outpourings of lava and gases originate near the mantle's upper boundary. Hot magma (molten rock) squeezes upwards, usually following fissures left by quakes, and sometimes erupts at once, sometimes remains for long periods in vast chambers within the crust before pushing to the surface. But exactly what triggers an eruption, science has not yet learned.

THE MULTILAYERED EARTH has a hot but solid inner core and a molten outer core—both probably composed of iron and nickel—a warm rocky mantle and thin cool crust.

THE STEAMING CRATER of Nyam-
lagira volcano in the Congo is a
scene of broken rock and clouds of
gas (*right*). From such vents in
the crust have come most of the
atmosphere and water on earth.

THE FIERY FOUNTAINS of Kilauea
in Hawaii (*below*) spew forth a
lava lake. In some places in the
crater the flow reaches a depth of
350 feet. Lava from thousands of
such eruptions built the islands.

47

THE EARTH'S VIBRATIONS after an earthquake are simulated as waves of colour sweeping through the interior of this two-inch disc. A sharp blow at the top of the model starts a shock wave (1), which spreads quickly through the entire disc (2 and 3), then gradually fades in a series of slow, rhythmic pulsations (4 to 8) until the stresses die out completely (9). In the model, photographed in polarized light in a New York University laboratory, the earth's rocky mantle is represented by a hard rubber ring, the molten outer core by gelatine and the solid inner core by an aluminium disc.

A STRAIN METER DEEP IN A MOUNTAIN TUNNEL USES A 75-FOOT QUARTZ ROD TO MEASURE EXPANSION AND CONTRACTION OF THE CRUST

The Pulse-Beats of the Earth

From laboratory experiments like the one shown on the opposite page and from instruments such as the earth-strain meter developed by Dr. Hugo Benioff of the California Institute of Technology (*above*), science is learning more about earthquakes and something about the continual, less evident stretching and compression of the earth's crust. The moon, for example, creates tides on solid land just as it does in the oceans: twice a day, with each tide, any point on earth may rise and fall several inches. Also, for days after a severe earthquake the earth vibrates at certain frequencies like a gong that has been struck. These frequencies are far too low to be audible—one "tone" is 20 octaves below middle C—but they are powerful. There is even speculation that they indirectly move the earth's inner core a fraction of an inch. Scientists are studying still other movements along fault lines, which they believe may help to forecast when and where earthquakes will strike.

FATHER JOSEPH LYNCH, A FAMOUS EARTHQUAKE STUDENT, WATCHES SEISMOGRAPHS IN FORDHAM'S UNDERGROUND OBSERVATORY

AN EARTHQUAKE'S SIGNATURE is written with a beam of light on a strip of photographic paper (*right*). This strip from one of Fordham's seismographs is marked off in minutes (Nos. 1-12), and was made on a drum that revolves every half-hour. From top to bottom, this portion thus spans five and a half hours. In the sixth half-hour line, the shocks of an earthquake appear: first the primary waves (P), followed by the slower secondary waves (S), and finally the surface waves (L). From the interval between the first two waves (5 minutes, 18 seconds), seismologists calculated how far away this quake was—in Montana, 2,195 miles from New York, on August 18, 1959.

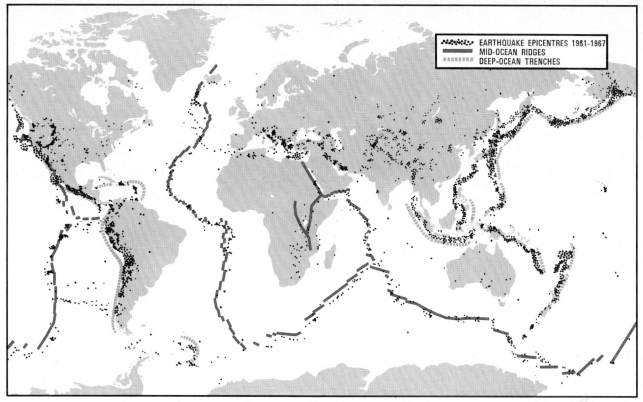

EARTHQUAKE EPICENTRES (DOTS) CONCENTRATE ALONG SEA TRENCHES (DASHED LINES) AND MID-OCEAN RIDGES (SOLID LINES)

Tracking down Earthquakes

When an earthquake occurs, its vibrations travel rapidly through the body of the earth. These vibrations are detected by seismographs that keep a ceaseless vigil all over the world, recording the earth's tremors as abrupt, zigzag lines on sensitized paper (*below*). By comparing data from several stations, seismologists can pin-point the disturbance and measure its force.

With their world-wide network of observatories, seismologists have found that the globe's seemingly solid, stolid mass is in an eternal tremble. And they have perceived a pattern to its shaking. Earthquake-prone areas lie along the dis-

tinctive heights and depths of the sea floor (*map above*). Although most quakes—and the most disastrous of them—originate a few miles down in the earth's crust, a number take place at an intermediate level in the mantle and some occur as deep as 446 miles. All these deep quakes occur in two main belts that generally follow the paths of the abyssal trenches in the Pacific Ocean off the coasts of South America and Asia. The trenches, scientists now believe, mark the places where gigantic moving sections of the earth's crust meet head-on and crunch over one another—a clash of great masses that is literally earth-shaking.

AN EXPOSED FAULT in western Nevada reveals where the earth's crust reared over 15 feet to relieve vast pressures from below. The sudden movement set off a localized earthquake in December 1954.

A TWISTED TRACK is bent by the movement of a California fault in 1906. Faults in many areas, as well as the San Andreas one, shifted in that year, when the San Francisco earthquake occurred.

A DEPARTMENT STORE LURCHES OVER AND BIG FIRES BREAK OUT

Death from a Violent Earth

The forces distorting the earth's crust are like the winding of an alarm clock—accumulating energy that will ultimately be released in a sudden burst of violence. A major earthquake expends much more energy than the most powerful man-made explosion. Its destructive effect may be magnified by landslides in the mountains, fires in the cities and huge waves at sea that can wreak death and damage thousands of miles from the original disturbance. Earthquakes rank

DURING A 1948 EARTHQUAKE THAT KILLED 3,895 IN FUKUI, JAPAN

A SUDDEN LANDSLIDE dumped this stretch of highway into Hebgen Lake, Montana, during the 1959 earthquake near Yellowstone Park, one of the most violent recorded in the U.S.A. It killed 28.

A STRANDED FLEET of small craft jams the streets of Shiogama, Japan, in the wake of tsunami waves. Formed by earthquakes in Chile in May 1960, the waves travelled 10,000 miles in 24 hours.

among the great disasters of history. The deadliest on record include: Shensi Province, China, 1556—830,000 dead; Calcutta, India, 1737—300,000 dead; Kansu Province, China, 1920—180,000 dead; Tokyo, Japan, 1923 —over 100,000 dead. The toll of the famous 1906 San Francisco earthquake was relatively low at 452. Claiming more than 12,000 victims each, earthquake disasters shattered the seaport of Agadir, Morocco, in 1960 and swept across rural northern Iran in 1962.

Drilling into the Ocean Bed

Beneath the deep oceans that cover two-thirds of the earth are concealed some of the most tantalizing secrets of our planet. There the crust of the earth is thinner and the unknown mantle—the layer beneath the crust—lies closest, tempting scientists to drill into it. The first such attempt, the ambitious Project Mohole, got under way during the 1960s and proved the value of deep-sea drilling with several test holes (*opposite*) before spiralling costs led to its cancellation.

Soon afterwards, however, work began on the more modest Deep Sea Drilling Project, which is not aimed at reaching the mantle but at exploring the crust itself. This venture uses a special ship, the *Glomar Challenger* (*left*), which can be held precisely in position in the sea—without any anchor—by sound-wave guiding systems and computer-controlled propellers. From this stable platform scientists lowered drilling pipes into waters four miles deep to scoop up cores of ocean sediment (*above*) and bedrock. Analysis of the fossil contents has indicated that the ocean floors spread, moving continents around the earth.

ALMOST FIVE MILES OF DRILLING PIPES can be carried on the decks of the 9,500-ton *Glomar Challenger* as it pursues its mission of drilling holes deep into the ocean bed.

AN ANXIOUS MOMENT comes as the shaft with its diamond-studded drill goes down through the centre well of *Cuss I*, the Project Mohole ship that pioneered deep-sea drilling.

3

Anatomy
of the Skies

THE sea that covers nearly three-quarters of the globe is only the second big-
gest thing on earth. Incomparably vaster is the ocean of the atmosphere,
which dominates the lives of men and all other creatures as surely as water
dominates the lives of fish. Without the atmosphere's oxygen, living things
die almost at once. Without rain erosion and the weathering of rocks, there
would be no soil for plants to grow in. Without carbon dioxide the plants
could not produce carbohydrates, the primary link in the food chain that
supports all animal life. Without the high-altitude umbrella of ozone to
absorb the lethal ultra-violet rays of the sun, human existence—if any—
would be quite different. Yet this is only a fractional list of the free services
performed by the atmosphere and taken for granted by more than 3,000
million human beings who at this moment are drawing breaths of it.

The atmosphere is an invisible and probably inexhaustible mixture of
air, water vapour and dust particles—including radioactive fall-out particles
from nuclear explosions and the miasma of pollutants from a technological
society. At sea level, the very bottom of the ocean of air, a cubic foot of
the mixture weighs about an ounce and a quarter. The entire atmosphere

weighs 5,100,000,000,000,000 tons, barely a millionth as much as the earth, and the force with which gravity holds it in place causes it to exert a pressure of 15 pounds to the square inch at sea level.

The human body copes with this burden by exerting an equal outward pressure to balance that of the atmosphere, just as fish do in order to live under far greater pressures deep in the ocean. The density of the air dwindles with increasing altitude, fading off into the virtual void of interplanetary space but remaining tangible enough to support aeroplanes and balloons for a dozen or so miles up.

UNTIL men and instruments could leave the ground to find out more, everything beyond the earth's thin shell of ordinary, breathable air was simply called the "ether", for want of a more accurate label. In recent years scientific views of the atmosphere have had to undergo repeated rapid revision, always in the direction of greater complexity. One contemporary way to classify the sky is to divide it into five regions, going out from the earth's surface: troposphere, stratosphere, mesosphere, ionosphere and exosphere. Three-quarters of the bulk of the whole envelope is concentrated in the bottom layer of the troposphere, along with the haze and dust, the clouds and storms—and all of life. Its upper boundary is the tropopause, fixed by hot-and-cold air exchanges at altitudes as low as five miles above the poles, as high as 10 miles above the equator. Within the tropospheric zone, air temperature drops nearly 2° C. with every 1,000 feet of elevation. The tropopause being lower at the poles, its temperature there falls only to about −50° C., but over the equator it falls to −73° C. Everywhere within the troposphere the air—hot or cold, dry or humid, thick or thin—is a constant mixture: nitrogen 78 per cent, oxygen 21 per cent, argon 0.9 per cent, carbon dioxide 0.03 per cent, with traces of half a dozen other gases, plus a variable load of water vapour.

Starting in the cold stratosphere, a layer extending 10 to 15 miles higher, and in the warmer (up to 10° C.) mesosphere, which goes up to the 50-mile level, there are crucial chemical changes in the air. In the first of these, ozone is added to the mixture. This is the same clean-smelling gas that is often noticeable around electrical generators and ultra-violet lights. It is "heavy oxygen", each of its molecules containing three atoms of oxygen, and it is formed when an electrical discharge or strong ultra-violet rays pass through ordinary oxygen. In the upper atmosphere, ozone soaks up much of the ultra-violet radiation streaming earthwards from the sun.

A cold front, the leading edge of an air mass whose cold air is dense and therefore heavy, advances from left to right below, driving under a lighter mass of warm air. As the warm air is displaced upwards, cooling reduces its capacity for moisture, and clouds and then rainfall are produced. Thus a cold front is often marked by a line of storm clouds.

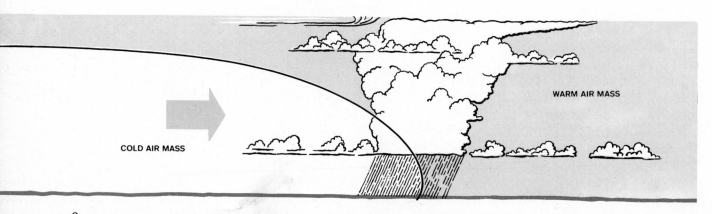

COLD AIR MASS

WARM AIR MASS

Every second, a million million million primary cosmic-ray particles, travellers from far outside the solar system, reach the neighbourhood of the earth, with a total power input of more than a thousand million watts. When they collide with the atmosphere's component atoms and molecules, the collisions produce showers of secondary particles. It is these "secondaries" that continue down to the earth's surface. Eight of them strike every square inch of the ground every minute; thousands strike every human being every hour. These particles are very penetrating; there is no escaping the ceaseless bombardment. But thanks to the break-up in the atmosphere, the barrage is harmless and has no perceptible influence on life. If they were primary cosmic rays, the effect would be lethal.

Starting at 50 miles and ending at 350 to 600 miles is the ionosphere, where more radical changes occur in the atmosphere. X-rays, as well as ultra-violet rays from the sun, ionize the rarefied air: they produce electrically charged (rather than neutral) atoms and molecules, together with unattached electrons. In this region, primarily a layer of oxygen, the temperature reaches nearly 1,100° C. But the air is so thin—the entire ionosphere, despite its huge size, contains only 0.001 per cent by weight of the atmosphere—that "temperature" has little practical meaning. No stationary object within this layer could absorb much heat from the rarefied air.

THE ionosphere's reflection of radio waves, which makes possible long-distance broadcasts, was understood decades ago, as was the service rendered by the lower, denser layers in incinerating nearly all the millions of meteors that rain down daily towards the earth. But it was not until man began his counter-barrage into space, with the rocket probes launched during and since the International Geophysical Year, that any real knowledge was gained of the exosphere, the outermost layer of all. Only in 1962 was one of its components, the magnetosphere, defined as a gigantic trap that imprisons sub-atomic particles from the sun. At about the same time, deep space probes disclosed something of the exosphere's composition: a 900-mile layer of thinly dispersed helium, surrounded by a layer of hydrogen that extends over 4,000 miles farther before tapering off into the emptiness of space. Atoms and molecules are so far apart in the exosphere that they seldom collide and, in fact, some escape from the earth for good.

From this quick tour, working from the inside out, it is apparent that the atmosphere is anything but inert. Its major action, among many, is to serve as an enormous engine, using the sun's radiation as a power source

Pushing along behind a cold air mass, a warm system of less dense—that is, lighter—air climbs up its trailing edge, forming a long slope and producing a broad band of rainfall, as the warm air rises and cools. Clouds soaring high above the cold air may appear as far as 1,000 miles in front of, and several days before, the arrival of the warm front they herald.

WARM AIR MASS

COLD AIR MASS

to drive the currents of air that stream and eddy around the earth. In other words, the atmosphere makes the winds and thereby the weather. To understand how this atmospheric engine operates, one should keep in mind that all bodies, at all temperatures, radiate electromagnetic waves of one kind or another. In order of decreasing wave-lengths, these include radio waves (long, short, on down to the microwaves used in radar); infra-red waves; the waves of visible light; ultra-violet waves; X-rays; and—shortest of all—gamma-rays.

All these waves have the same physical nature, but their different lengths result in rather different behaviour. The hotter an object is, the more electro-magnetic energy it emits and the shorter the average wave-length. The heat of the sun's surface is such that its predominant radiation is in the visible light range of wave-lengths. However, the troposphere—in the confines of which most of what we call "weather" takes place—is not directly affected by these light rays. Instead, whatever solar radiation that may escape being reflected back into space by dust or clouds, or being absorbed by the ozone layer, passes straight through the lower levels of the atmosphere until it strikes—and warms—the earth's land and water surface.

The earth accepts these solar rays and, in turn, gives off radiation largely of the longer, infra-red wave-lengths. Both the carbon dioxide and the water vapour in the atmosphere are excellent absorbers of infra-red; as a result, they take up nearly all such energy that radiates from the earth's surface. The entire troposphere becomes heated in this way. The ultimate source of this heat is the sun, since its rays warm the earth's surface and maintain its infra-red radiation. None the less, the actual heating of the atmosphere is from below, as with a pot on a stove, and not from above.

A low-pressure cell, shown above by iso-baric lines that connect points of equal pressure, can form if a mass of cold air envelops a centre of light, warm air. Given a counter-clockwise twist by the earth's rotation, the air spirals inwards (arrows, below) towards the centre of low pressure, causing rainfall in the shaded areas, as the warm, moist air rises and cools.

THE earth is not uniformly warmed everywhere by the sun's rays and thus its surface is not everywhere equally radiant. As we have seen, sunlight arrives at the earth nearly vertically in the equatorial zone, but at an oblique angle near the poles, so equatorial air is much warmer than polar air. It is this difference in temperature that turns the atmosphere into a heat engine, causing the winds to blow. If the earth did not rotate, these air currents would be quite orderly: warm air near the equator would rise and flow towards the poles, while cold air at the poles would sink and flow towards the equator in an endless, interchanging cycle. The earth's rotation modifies this simple pattern: in each hemisphere, working away from the pole and towards the equator, there is first a westward drift of air in the lower atmosphere, then an eastward one in mid-latitudes, and finally another westward drift near the equator. Each hemisphere's pattern of air flow is a mirror image of the other's: the easterly winds of the northern tropics—the trade winds—blow from the north-east, while the same easterly trades below the equator blow from the south-east. The name "trade wind" originated in the days of sail, when these steady winds were the mainstays of ocean commerce.

The westerly winds of middle latitudes do not share the trade winds' regular, stable pattern. Instead, they work up into immense high-altitude eddies, thousands of miles across. Below these large-scale eddies (three to six of which are over each hemisphere at any one time) are many smaller ones that swirl about for a few hours or days before they vanish and are replaced by others. The larger eddies are more persistent: one of them may move eastwards for weeks before losing its identity in random turbulence. The birth and growth of these swirls of wind account for the changeable weather of the earth's middle latitudes.

A smaller eddy that forms around a centre of low-pressure air acquires a rotary motion and starts to spin—counter-clockwise in the Northern Hemisphere and clockwise in the Southern. Such a spinning eddy is called a "cyclone", but is not necessarily the storm wind that is sometimes given the same name. Here is a chance to watch the atmosphere's heat engine in action on a small scale. Why does a cyclone spin? The air at its centre is lighter—lower in pressure—while the air surrounding the eddy is heavier—higher in pressure. Thus, the heavier air flows *inwards*, towards the centre, and it is this inward flow that is deflected by the earth's rotation. Consider the opposite case: here, the eddy forms around a deep, dense air mass at higher pressure than the air around it, and the air flow is therefore *outwards* from its centre. In consequence, the spin is in exactly the opposite direction and such an eddy is known as an "anticyclone".

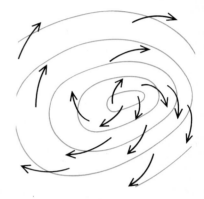

These great whorls of air make the major marks on weather maps. The United States is often swept in winter by anticyclones from northern Canada that are very cold and dry. When such a cold-air mass lies over a region, the weather will be correspondingly cold and clear, with the possibility of some cumulus clouds in the afternoon, because of the heating of the earth by the sun. In summer, moist cyclones from the Gulf of Mexico often dominate weather in the eastern United States, producing hot, humid, windless days.

A high-pressure cell is formed by a process exactly the reverse of that which creates a low-pressure cell (opposite). A mass of cold, dense air tends to sink and spread out (above), replacing lighter surrounding air. As it spirals outwards (arrows, below) from its centre of high pressure, the cold air, given a clockwise twist by the earth's rotation, brings clear skies.

The line of contact between two air masses of different temperature is called a "front". A cold front represents cold air replacing warmer air; a warm front moves in such a way that warm air replaces cold. The warm air along a front of either kind cools as it rises, producing cloudiness and rainfall. This effect is more pronounced along a cold front, which leads to more violent storms. The approach and passage of a front is one of the most fascinating of meteorological events. A warm front is signalled by cirrus clouds (mare's-tails) high up in the sky. These represent the condensed moisture at the leading edge of the oncoming warm air that has overrun the retreating cold air. Soon a milky film of cirro-stratus covers the sky, and some hours later the ominous grey veils of alto-stratus clouds appear. Then low, thick, dark nimbo-stratus clouds darken the sky and rain begins to fall. Finally the warm air completely replaces the cold, from top to bottom, the temperature steadies and the rain stops. More or less steady weather follows then until the approach of the next front.

THE sequence of events when a cold front arrives is faster and more dramatic. The cold oncoming air is too heavy to override the warm air in its path, and instead burrows underneath. Forced upwards by the intruding cold-air mass, the warm, moisture-laden air condenses, forming a great vertical bank of dense cumulo-nimbus clouds. A well-defined cold front typically appears as a squall line of dark, ominous clouds, straight as a ruler from horizon to horizon, sweeping in from the west or north-west. When it strikes, the wind shifts abruptly from south-west to north-west, the temperature falls and a torrent of heavy rain begins, driven by strong, irregular gusts. A violent thunderstorm may occur, adding sight and sound to the tempestuous proceedings. After half an hour or so the squall-line is almost out of sight to the east, and a band of clear sky appears in the west. Then the north-west wind blows more steadily and dry, cool, clear weather sets in. Of course, not all cold fronts bring with them such boisterous effects, but the pattern is familiar to dwellers in the middle latitudes.

The turbulent, unstable atmosphere near a squall-line sometimes produces a vortex of rapidly spinning air. The vortex appears as a narrow, funnel-shaped cloud that extends to the ground, but its modest aspect conceals winds of hundreds of miles an hour. A vortex of this kind is called a "tornado" on land and a "waterspout" over the ocean; very little is known about conditions inside the whirlwinds, because any instruments that have happened to be in their paths have invariably been destroyed.

Few people have looked such a whirlwind in the eye and lived to tell about it. One who did was Will Keller, a Kansas farmer who dared to peer out of his storm cellar as a tornado passed over in 1928. Above him was the hollow vortex, 50 to 100 feet across, its walls lit by zigzag lightning flashes. Smaller vortexes were forming inside the main one and emitting hissing noises as they broke free of it. In 1955, a motorist encountered a thick dust-cloud on the road near Scottsbluff, Nebraska. Realizing it was no ordinary dust cloud, he stopped his car. Then, according to a report in the U.S. Weather Bureau's *Monthly Weather Review*, "there was a roar and a crash of glass as the windshield and windows were broken. . . . He pulled his wife's head over in his lap and bent over to shield their faces. There was a moment of comparative calm and he raised his head to peer through the broken windshield. Large boards, tree limbs, and a boulder the size of a man's head were floating around the car . . . there was a crash and that is all he remembers until he regained consciousness in a hospital. Actually, both occupants were thrown from the car. . . . The wife was apparently killed instantly. The car was rolled into an unshapen mass of metal."

Usually a tornado is a few hundred yards across and travels at perhaps 25 miles an hour for a distance anywhere from a fraction of a mile to 100 miles or more before it vanishes. The central United States is probably the most tornado-prone part of the world, and there they form so rapidly and unpredictably as to make protection against them chiefly a matter of descending into a strong storm cellar whenever a thunderstorm appears. Waterspouts are generally milder than tornadoes, though still capable of violent destruction. The lower portion of a spout contains some salt water drawn up from the sea beneath it, but is mostly made up of fresh water that has condensed out of its basic body of cloud. Some waterspouts range up to a mile in height.

Many localities have other peculiar winds of their own that are more or less unrelated to the global pattern. Simple examples are the sea and land breezes familiar along many coast-lines. These winds owe their existence to the fact that the temperature of the ocean surface stays fairly constant, while that of the land surface may fluctuate widely. On a hot day a beach becomes warm and the air above it rises, while cooler, denser air from over the water —the sea breeze—is drawn in to replace it. At night the beach cools rapidly and the air circulation is reversed: the air over the land is now denser, and a land breeze flows off shore.

The sea and land breezes' bigger relatives are the monsoons of Asia, which are governed by the contrasts in land and sea temperatures in summer and winter instead of in day-time and night-time. In winter the Asiatic plateau is bitterly cold, so that the overlying air is much denser than that above the China Sea and Indian Ocean to its east and south. A steady, cold, dry wind blows off-shore from October to April, deflected by the earth's rotation into a north-east wind in the China Sea and northern part of the Indian Ocean. During the summer Asia swelters, and the air above it rises, while cooler air moves in from the ocean. This summer monsoon brings air that has picked up considerable moisture on its sea passage, and its arrival deluges south-east Asia with prolonged, drenching rain. A monsoon climate of this kind has only two varieties of weather, wet in summer and dry in winter, in contrast to the fickleness of middle-latitude weather.

Other regional winds are conditioned by landscape as well as temperature. Cold, dry air may spill over a mountain range suddenly after having collected on the windward side of the range for some time, surging down into adjacent valleys with great force. The mistral consists of cold air from the Rhône Glacier that pours down the Rhône Valley to the sea for much of the year, while the bora of the Adriatic has a similar origin in the mountains of Yugoslavia. The geography of the Mediterranean, bordered by high mountains on the north and the hot Sahara on the south, is responsible for a number of notorious winds. At times a hot wind from the Sahara, the sirocco, blows north across the Mediterranean, accumulating enough water vapour to bring rain to Sicily and the Italian coast.

THOSE who live along the fringes of the world's oceans have good reason to fear the coming of autumn, when tropical cyclones are most likely to be formed at sea, to mature as they move in the grip of the trade winds, and to cause disaster if they sweep over the land. The western shores of the North Atlantic, North and South Pacific, and Indian Oceans are most often the targets of tropical cyclones, but they are unknown only in the South Atlantic and eastern part of the South Pacific. These violent tropical storms are quite infrequent (only 48 occur on the average each year in the entire world), but their high power sets them apart, together with earthquakes, as the most destructive of natural phenomena.

At birth, one of these typhoons, or hurricanes, forms as a zone of low atmospheric pressure over a tropical ocean. Warm air laden with moisture flows towards this zone and ascends within it. The water vapour in the rising column of warm air condenses into clouds and rain, liberating a great deal of heat in the process, which further speeds the upward flow of air. Perhaps a quarter of a million tons of water are extracted from the ocean and the converging air every *second* by a hurricane, and their condensation over one day releases energy equivalent to the explosion of a 13,000-megaton nuclear bomb. As the heated air rises faster and faster, new air converges on the storm centre with ever-increasing speed; winds of as much as 200 miles per hour may be generated in this way. The rotation of the earth deflects wind flowing towards the storm centre to the right in the Northern Hemisphere and to the left in the Southern, leading respectively to the counterclockwise and clockwise circulation already noted in the cyclones of the middle latitudes. At the centre of a hurricane is an area of calm, a few miles across, called the "eye". A ring of dense clouds, from which a deluge of rain falls, surrounds the eye, and in this ring the winds are at their most furious; the wind speed may change by a hundred miles an hour or more in a distance of a mile within the ring.

The hurricane itself is a nightmare of shrieking wind made all the more apocalyptic by torrents of rain and darkness, as dense clouds blot out the sky. If the "eye" passes overhead the turmoil comes to a crescendo and abruptly stops; the wind falls to a breeze, the rain ceases and bits of blue sky appear through thin, patchy clouds. But the lull is brief and soon the full fury of the storm strikes again, now with the wind from the opposite direction. The recession of the hurricane is marked by a sequence of weather exactly the reverse of the events heralding its approach.

Such a storm is kept going by the heat and water vapour which it sucks from the sea's surface, and it weakens and smartly disappears when deprived of this power supply. Thus hurricanes seldom penetrate far inland, and if they miss land entirely by swinging polewards, the colder water in their paths before long quenches their violence.

IN a single year the engine of the atmosphere, using such forceful instruments as typhoons and monsoons and such peaceful ones as sunlight, lifts 100,000 cubic miles of water into the air from the seas and the continents. Everything that goes up in this massive evaporation process must eventually come down, and most of it falls as rain. In order that rain, snow, sleet or hail should fall, clouds must form. Even air that is supersaturated with moisture cannot usually produce clouds, unless myriads of minute "condensation nuclei" are present. The nuclei may be salt particles from sea spray, or fine dust, or smoke particles from forest fires and industrial plants, or the combustion products of volcanoes—or even the water-attracting oxides of nitrogen left behind by lightning. It has been estimated that Krakatoa's 1883 eruption filled the atmosphere with enough condensation nuclei to provide 1,000 worldwide rainy days.

The water-vapour molecules that join a nucleus form cloud droplets (or ice crystals, if the air is well below freezing). These cannot fall as rain: they hold only a millionth as much water as an ordinary raindrop. In absolutely still air they would take eight hours to fall a quarter of a mile, and in moving air they are hardly affected by gravity at all. It is their growth to bigger size, called "coalescence", that makes rainfall possible. In turbulent air bigger droplets collide with and "collect" smaller ones; in cold air, droplets evaporate and then condense on near-by ice crystals.

Only when a droplet grows to raindrop size, at least 1/125th of an inch in diameter, can it fall out of the cloud. It may never reach the ground; often a torrent may spill out of clouds high above a desert, only to evaporate entirely on the way down. Raindrops that reach the earth in a fine spray, called "drizzle", have fallen from relatively low clouds, with little time to collide with other drops while falling. The raindrops that arrive in a vigorous downpour come from deep clouds where the colliding of droplets, and the "capturing" of little ones by bigger ones, is going on quite actively.

For snow to form, a cloud must be chilled to a temperature of about -15 to $-20°$ C. The cloud droplets are supercooled and freeze together into crystals. Because the crystals carry a thin film of unfrozen water, they collect into snowflakes when they collide. In extreme cold the crystals are drier and fall as granular snow. Rain that starts in warm air and falls through a cold layer does not turn into snow, but into the translucent ice pellets called sleet. Frozen raindrops from high clouds, moving through a thunderstorm and hurled about in violent updraughts, pick up concentric layers of snow and ice. Finally they plummet to earth as hailstones, pea-sized or golf-ball-sized, depending on their rough-and-tumble experiences above.

A RARE RED-GREEN AURORA FLAMES OVER CONNECTICUT. RADIATION FROM SPACE MAKES THE UPPER AIR GLOW LIKE A NEON TUBE

The Shield of the Air

Intangible and invisible, the atmosphere envelops the earth like a protective shell. It screens us from the lethal rays of the sun and most of the bombarding cosmic rays from space. It incinerates most meteors before they reach the surface. It insulates the world from the cold of space and hoards the warmth bestowed by the sun. Even when unleashing storms, it is a zone of majestic beauty.

65

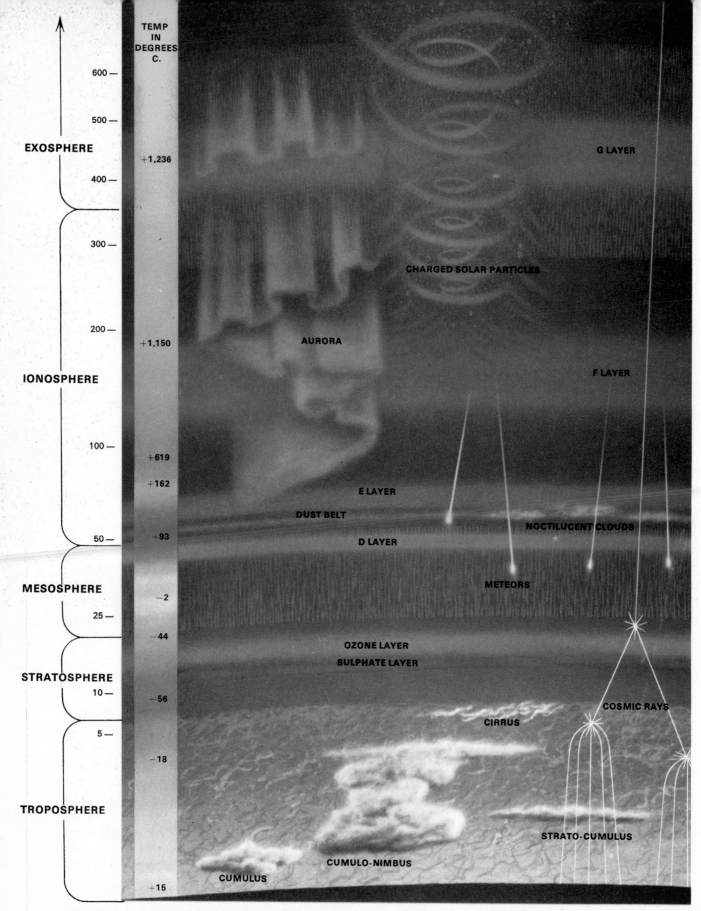

EXOSPHERE

IONOSPHERE

MESOSPHERE

STRATOSPHERE

TROPOSPHERE

TEMP
IN
DEGREES
C.

600 —

500 —

+1,236

400 —

300 —

200 —   +1,150

100 —   +619
             +162

50 —   −93

             −2

25 —

             −44

10 —   −56

5 —

             −18

             +15

G LAYER

CHARGED SOLAR PARTICLES

AURORA

F LAYER

E LAYER

DUST BELT

NOCTILUCENT CLOUDS

D LAYER

METEORS

OZONE LAYER

SULPHATE LAYER

CIRRUS

COSMIC RAYS

STRATO-CUMULUS

CUMULO-NIMBUS

CUMULUS

THE FIRST 600 MILES of the atmosphere, mapped in this cross-section, are a complex succession of air layers. The gradations at the left show how temperatures fall and then rise with increasing altitude. At the upper levels, auroras appear like hanging curtains. The spiral swirl is a thrust of particles from the deep radiation zone of the magnetosphere.

66

A PACIFIC SUNSET SPREADS BANDS OF COLOUR OVER THE HORIZON. THE LOWER ATMOSPHERE SPLITS THE SUN'S RAYS LIKE A PRISM

The Many-Layered Atmosphere

The atmosphere is neither as simple as it looks from below nor as shallow as scientists recently supposed. The troposphere, where man exists, is merely the lowest level of many. It ends at 5 to 10 miles up and contains the air currents which shape most of the earth's weather. The stratosphere occupies the next 10 to 15 miles. In it are two narrow layers containing gas molecules not found elsewhere in the atmosphere. The lower contains particles of certain sulphates which may play a role in rainfall. Above it is the vital layer of ozone, a form of oxygen, which absorbs most of the deadly ultra-violet rays coming from the sun and thus makes life possible on the earth. Next is the mesosphere, a warm layer in which most of the meteors from outer space are incinerated. It is replaced, at 50 miles, by the ionosphere, whose top fades out somewhere between 350 and 600 miles up. Auroras flicker in the ionosphere and near its bottom float noctilucent clouds which may sometimes be seen glimmering at dawn or dusk. The lettered layers are zones where air particles have been ionized by solar radiation. They are important to man because they reflect certain radio waves back to earth, making short-wave reception possible.

Last comes the exosphere, where the atmosphere gradually thins to almost nothing. It contains a huge radiation band known as the magnetosphere, and is believed to extend to 40,000 miles.

67

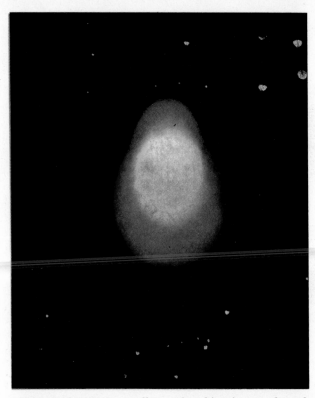

LOW-LYING VENUS, usually pearly white, is seen through atmospheric distortion as a multi-coloured, pear-shaped body. As with the sun, green is dominant on top and red below.

The Flash Phenomena

Like the oceans of water, the ocean of air is in constant motion, and all light coming to the earth from space is blurred by its ripples. Up to now, astronomers have only been able to see out dimly through the atmosphere. Until telescopes can be set beyond the atmosphere, in space or on the moon, what man sees in the sky must often be a mirage. Viewed at sunrise or sunset through the rippled air, the sun, for instance, may sometimes appear as fluffy as a cloud, flattened and perhaps seeming to split into thin horizontal strips. The sun's colours will vary from the blinding white of noon to soft red or violet hues tinting the horizon. Sometimes the setting sun may unleash a flash of red below or green on top, like the almost instantaneous lighting and blowing-out of millions of candles. These bursts of colour are caused by special atmospheric conditions when the sun is close to the horizon.

The remarkable photographs here, taken from the Vatican Observatory at Castel Gandolfo in Italy, prove that the flash mirage lies not in the beholder's eye, as some scientists have suggested, but rather is a result of the way the atmosphere affects light. The golden white light of the sun is actually a mixture of all the colours of the rainbow. It happens that green light rays are more affected by travel through the air than the red ones, which are only slightly distorted. When the sun is low on the horizon at sunset, its light must pass a long distance through the earth's atmosphere. The red rays in it tend to disappear first below the horizon, while the green rays, which have been bent in their passage through the air, remain visible. Under certain conditions, the red and green actually appear to separate. When they do, the so-called green flash is created. Rarely, the flash may last for several minutes.

Similar atmospheric interference often affects the light coming from bright bodies much smaller than the sun, such as Venus. When it is near the horizon, this planet is sometimes distorted into ever-changing, overlapping images that are brilliantly splashed with the flash-pattern colours.

A BLUE-TOPPED SUN is created by a light bulb in a glass globe to simulate a sunset's distortions. A blue flash sometimes occurs with a green one, but is much less prominent.

SOFT PLUMES of cirrus clouds float four to eight miles over the earth. They are fair-weather clouds unless they thicken into the hazy cirro-stratus form that signals impending rain.

GREY LAYERS of strato-cumulus loom as a menacing front advancing on a clear sky. Composed of rolls or folds, and at times patchy, they threaten rain but do not always deliver it.

The Benign and Furious
Moods of the Clouds

Clouds have always been heralds of fair or foul weather. They are made of water vapour that has evaporated from the earth and formed droplets or ice crystals of microscopic size in the atmosphere. Of too light a weight to descend as rain, the droplets may ride the air currents indefinitely before they condense around dust, salt or other

A TORRENTIAL RAIN BEATS DOWN UPON THE SOUTH PACIFIC OFF SAMOA. THE BALEFUL-LOOKING CLOUD MASS FROM WHICH IT IS FALLING

A THIN CLOUD-CAP hovers in fixed position over Mount Kilimanjaro, Tanzania. It is formed into a lens shape by draughts of air sweeping up and down the mountain slopes.

A BOLD THUNDER-HEAD of cumulo-nimbus gives warning of an approaching storm. Flung high by fast-rising air currents, the frozen top is hammered anvil-flat by a warm layer above.

particles. Clouds were first classified in 1803 according to the Latin names for their shapes: *cirrus* for ringlet, *cumulus* for heap and *stratus* for scattering. The term *nimbus*, for rainstorm, was applied later. In varying combinations, the terms describe the patterns of the clouds. The fragile cirrus clouds spray out as high as 40,000 feet.

Cirro-cumulus crowd the sky like mackerel scales at 20,000 to 40,000 feet, while cirro-stratus appear as a milky blur. Cumulo-nimbus are thunder-heads that rise to great heights. Cumulus are fleecy white puffs 4,000 to 6,500 feet up. Nimbo-stratus are drizzle clouds, and strato-cumulus are the low-flying messengers of rain or snow.

IS THE BOTTOM OF A THUNDERSTORM CUMULO-NIMBUS FORMATION WHICH MAY EXTEND FROM SEA-LEVEL TO AN ALTITUDE OF 40,000 FEET

A BRILLIANT FOUNTAIN arcs from the Arizona desert as a rainbow appears. It is caused by sunlight passing from behind the viewer through drops of moisture. The drops act as prisms, splitting the white light of the sun into its many component colours. Colours are brightest when the water droplets are the largest, often after a summer thunder-shower.

Magical Mists in the Air

Two of the most striking phenomena that occur in the earth's lower atmosphere are thick, dim fogs and brilliant rainbows. Rainbows (*opposite*) are caused when the sun's rays strike a heavy but translucent cloud of raindrops left hanging in the air after a shower. This thin film of moisture acts as a prism, separating and reflecting the whole spectrum of visible colour that is contained in sunlight.

Fogs are also the result of heavy concentrations of water vapour. They form most frequently when the air just above ground-level cools suddenly and condenses its load of water vapour into tiny droplets about 0.1 millimetre across. The most persistent fogs occur when air temperatures are "inverted", that is, when the cool ground air is overlaid with warmer air and cannot move away. When this condition exists over a densely inhabited region that produces a good deal of smoke and other fumes, a noxious smog results.

A GROUND FOG obscures the earth like vapours of steam, turning an English landscape into a Japanese print. Such a morning mist along gentle slopes is a sign of fair weather ahead. Already, the sun's rays are piercing the fog to disperse it. Like dew and frost, ground fog develops in the hours after midnight, often on windless autumnal nights.

73

Darting Fingers from the Sky

Before or during almost all of the 44,000 thunderstorms that beat down on the earth each day, darting fingers of light streak through the air, usually followed by claps of thunder. This is the anger of the skies—heard and seen—which made men fear the ancient thunderbolt-hurling gods. Lightning is still a violent, fearsome thing. It may come in great sheets, in balls or in zigzag or forked streaks. The accompanying rumbling of thunder is produced by the sudden expansion of air that has been heated by the bolt; thunder is heard after a flash because light travels faster than sound. The flashes result from atmospheric

A FREAKISH FLASH of lightning is attracted to a pillar of water flung up by the detonation of a U.S. Navy depth charge. A camera recording test-blasts caught the bolt by accident.

A TRIPLE BOLT is made by three consecutive flashes of lightning. All three, discharged within thousands of a second, follow parallel courses through the already ionized air.

A STREAKED SKY is seen from inside a ranger look-out tower in Clearwater National Forest, Idaho. The camera shutter was left open for two minutes, photographing a number of bursts of electricity, which may leap between different clouds or between sky and earth, wherever sufficient tension from opposite charges is built up. Erect structures on the earth's surface attract the ground-seeking bolts. To avoid fire, lightning rods are set on top of high buildings to "coax" the bolts and conduct their electric charges, as high as 100 million volts, to metal plates in the ground. Death by lightning comes to more than 150 persons in the U.S.A. every year, but on the beneficent side, lightning brings nitrogen from the air to the earth by converting it to an oxide, which then falls with the rain to fertilize the soil.

separate lightning flashes. The thickest ones are closest to the tower; the thinner ones thread out in the distance. Lightning starts about 10,000 forest fires a year in the U.S.A.

A SPIRAL OF FLAME streaks earthwards during a thunderstorm in Switzerland. This rare bolt has ignited chemicals in the atmosphere, giving it the appearance of twisted cloth.

A TWISTER'S TIP thunders along a Texas highway, flinging bits of destroyed houses into the air. Many tornadoes often whirl through the air at the same time. A dozen other funnels were counted in the area where this one struck.

The Ferocious Winds

The strongest winds that blow upon the earth's surface are those that whirl within the vortex of a tornado. Australia and North America know them best. About 150 tornadoes hit the U.S.A. each year, converging on the southern states in the spring and on mid-west states in summer. A tornado's funnel starts (usually after a thunderstorm) as a drift of clouds gently whirling downwards. When it gathers force and touches land, tons of dust and debris travel up the funnel, which may revolve at 200 to 500 miles an hour. The inverted whirlpool of air can lift an entire house and deposit it elsewhere, intact or in smithereens. Tornadoes also form at sea, where they are known as waterspouts. These are much less violent and do little damage.

A TORNADO'S WAKE in a suburb of Kansas City, Missouri (*below*), shows a broad, clean-cut lane of destruction. The width of such a path varies widely, from a few feet to 450 yards, extending as the vortex veers from side to side.

A DEMOLISHED BARN litters an Iowa farmyard after a tornado. Most of the damage from such storms is caused when buildings "explode" in the extreme low-air pressure of the tornado's centre. But objects in the buildings may remain untouched. In this case, five horses are still standing in their stalls moments after the debris stopped falling.

A HURRICANE EYE, five miles wide, is seen in the centre of these strips filmed by a U-2 reconnaissance plane flying at 65,000 feet. The main force of the storm is below 50,000 feet.

The Violence of Wind and Wave

To man and his flimsy structures, wind-driven water is among the most dangerous of natural phenomena. Since 1900 more than 50,000 persons have been killed as the ocean has licked over the land. The friction of air passing over the surface of water, as gentle as this rubbing of gas and liquid may seem, is enough to heap it into waves. The height of waves is proportional to wind speed: an 80-mile wind blowing uninterruptedly over the ocean raises 40-foot rolling seas. The highest waves tower to 100 feet and result when two smaller swells merge at sea.

Sometimes, as at the right, a monstrous wave will glide across many miles of ocean and pile up on the coast with little or no trace of the wind that started it on its way. More often, the great whirling motions of the atmosphere stir up storms at sea, which strike the shore with huge breakers and winds ranging from 75 to 200 miles an hour blowing around a central area of calm. There are several names for these whirlpool-like storms. In the Far East, they are called typhoons; in the Philippines, *baguios*; and in the Western Hemisphere, hurricanes—after the ancient thunder-god of the Carib Indians, Hurakan.

A VIOLENT WAVE 60 feet high, caused by a north-easter, crashes against the sea wall at Winthrop, Massachusetts. Although the wind has died away, the sea is still agitated.

4

The Crust that Floats

Until recently, both the earth itself and the sciences that dealt with it were accepted as fairly stable subjects. The earth's main features were thought to have been fixed in primordial times and, by now, only essentially local alterations seemed to be under way as the result of erosion, volcanic action and earthquakes. The earth sciences were in much the same calm state as the subject they studied. The earth sciences, notably geology, geophysics and oceanography, catalogued their observations about the earth—its continents and seas, its volcanoes and earthquakes, its rock types and locations—but found little to connect these observations into a meaningful and convincing story. They found peculiarities, such as beds of tropical coal in Antarctica or identical fossils on widely separated continents, and strained for explanations that even the explainers found hard to believe.

Within the past few years all this has changed. Most earth scientists now believe they are finally on the track of a general theory about the formation of the earth we know. Though obviously still incomplete, this theory seems to explain how the familiar features of the land and sea came into being, and how they will change in the future. It is already invigorating the earth sciences and tearing down old barriers between disciplines. In a few years, this theory has revealed our earth to be both a relatively simple and an almost unimaginably powerful mechanism.

Though much is not yet understood about the new dynamism that has been uncovered, what is already known provides pieces to many a puzzle. The recent discoveries confirm a centuries-old, oft-derided suspicion that entire continents drift around on the earth's surface. They provide plausible explanations for the formation of mountains and continents and for earthquakes and volcanoes. And they help to clear up such mysteries as why there have been ice-ages and why coal beds are today found in Antarctica.

Intimations of these new ideas have been glimpsed from time to time for centuries. When the first crude maps of the New World began emerging from the great voyages of exploration some 350 years ago, Sir Francis Bacon was the first to make a critical observation, one that has been rediscovered by many a schoolboy since. Bacon noted that the continents of South America and Africa look almost as though they might have been sawn apart along their Atlantic coastlines with a jigsaw.

IN later years many scientists puzzled over this appearance. During the 1920s a persistent German meteorologist named Alfred Wegener attained popular fame—and professional notoriety—from his dedicated espousal of the theory of "Continental Drift". The matching coastlines of Africa and South America, Wegener suggested, meant that once there was a single, giant, continental land mass he called Pangaea, sitting all alone on a globe covered by a single ocean called Panthalassa. In time, Pangaea cracked apart, and the pieces wandered away from one another to produce the continents of today. In fact, he contended, this continental wandering was still going on. Wegener marshalled other evidence to back his theory. He pointed to the similar plants and animals that are known to have existed in widely separated regions throughout geologic history. How did they get so far apart? A common explanation was the supposed existence of land bridges linking the continents, but the notion is hard to accept, if for no other reason than that there is no trace today of most of the supposed bridges, which must have been substantial affairs if they were to persist for hundreds of millions of years. But there was no need to dream up land bridges if the living things had stayed put while their land homes had moved.

Wegener had more to go on than some out-of-place fossils and matching coastlines. By the time he was preaching his drift theory, the continents' structure—if not their origin—was fairly well understood. Wegener and other scientists as well knew that the continents of the earth are immense plateaux of rock. Ordinary maps, which divide land from sea at the tidal zone, do not give a true picture of the continents, for they fail to show the gently sloping undersea margins that form the natural continuations of most coastlines. These continental shelves extend out to sea in shallow water for as much as 100 miles. It is the precipitous brinks of the continental shelves that are the true limits of the continents. Furthermore, under their thin layer of dirt the continents are really giant blocks of practically solid granite. They differ utterly from the deep sea floors which, under their layers of sediment, are almost solid basalt.

On a world average, the continents protrude almost three miles above the ocean floors today. Moreover, what evidence there is strongly suggests that this elevation, or a comparable one, has persisted since the continents' origin. What, then, keeps these weighty continental blocks from sinking downwards until they are level with the rest of the earth's crust? Even the most rigid shell of basalt could not withstand the constant pressure of such enormous masses of granite. The answer to this appears to be the same as the answer to why a cork floats: in both cases, the bodies are buoyant because they are less dense than the material in which they are immersed. In the case of the continents, it is the earth's mantle that plays water to these colossal corks. Granite is about 20 per cent lighter than the material of which the upper mantle is composed. Basalt, on the other hand, is only 10 per cent lighter. The continents thus *must* ride higher above the mantle than does the crust's basaltic basement layer.

ANOTHER problem presents itself in this picture of the continents as huge floating bodies of light granite. A cork does not float entirely *on* water but partly *in* it. A block of wood, being heavier than cork, will float deeper. How deep is determined by a simple law discovered 2,200 years ago by Archimedes: if the block of wood weighs a pound, it will float just deep enough to displace a pound of water. Thus it is not hard to see that a cork or a block of wood, being less dense than water, is actually held up by the water. In the same way, do the great blocks of granite that compose the continents have roots substantial enough to be floating like corks?

There are two ways of investigating this point. The first utilizes the same principles that enabled scientists to work out the sequence of the layers of the earth by measuring earthquake waves. By making very accurate measurements of the movements of quakes in the crust, it is possible to perceive vague outlines of the structure of the crust. The second method makes use of gravity measurements. Extremely sensitive instruments will detect differences in gravity at different points on the earth's surface, and since the force of gravity depends on the amount of matter near by, these differences indicate the varying amounts of granite and basalt that lie unreachably below. Both approaches yield the same conclusion: the continents indeed have massive roots that reach deep down to support the three miles or so that these blocks extend above the ocean floor.

A simplified model of the crust used by many geophysicists in their calculations supposes a more or less uniform, three-mile-thick layer of basalt on top of the mantle. Upon this are superimposed continental blocks, an average of 20 miles thick. The blocks are so heavy that they press the underlying basalt layer down about 14 miles into the mantle, thus making the mantle's surface slightly dimpled rather than perfectly spherical. So, although the continents cover only a trifle over a quarter of the earth's surface area, in terms of total volume they actually comprise about two-thirds of the crust, and the basaltic basement rock about one-third.

The idea that a continent—or indeed any major land mass, such as a large island—floats on the mantle is known as the theory of isostasy. A direct verification of the theory is found in the fact that the entire Scandinavian Peninsula is rising in the air. Pressed down by the weight of glaciers during the ice-age, it has been rising ever since the glaciers departed 9,000 years ago. Scandinavia is now believed to stand nearly a thousand feet higher than it did under the burden of the ice cap, and parts of it

The cycles through which rock disintegrates into sediment and the sediment is compressed into new rock are illustrated in the diagram above. Sediment (2) is formed of particles from all kinds of rock, plus the shells or other remains of animals. It is compressed, primarily, into sandstone and limestone (3), shale and conglomerate.

These sedimentary rocks may erode or they may be changed by heat, chemical action or pressure into metamorphic rock like marble or schist (4). These, remelting, can contribute material to igneous rocks (1) which are formed of molten matter. These igneous rocks, in turn, may be changed into metamorphic rock or may be eroded into new supplies of sediment.

are currently going up at the rate of three feet a century. Some estimates indicate it still has about 650 feet to go before it reaches equilibrium.

Just as the roots of continental blocks thrust deep enough to dimple the underlying mantle, so the roots of major mountain systems push down even deeper in order to support their weight and to justify their greater height. The first suspicion that mountains, as well as thrusting up, also extend down into the earth, came from gravity measurements performed in the 18th century with no more complex an instrument than a plumb-bob. On a level plain, where the earth's mass is more or less uniformly distributed, a plumb-bob points directly down, towards the centre of the earth. One would expect that near a mountain—a local concentration of the earth's mass—the plumb-line would be deflected by the extra gravitational pull of the mountain. In 1738, the French mathematician Pierre Bouguer went to an Andean peak—Mount Chimborazo, in what is now Ecuador—on an expedition sent by the French Academy to help to settle scientific arguments over the length of a meridian arc. While making gravitational measurements on Mount Chimborazo, he noticed that the gravitational attraction of the mountain caused a much smaller deflection of his plumb-bob than would be expected from such a great mass.

BOUGUER suspected that the granites in the mountain and under it were for some reason comparatively light-weight. He noted in his journal that it was as if the mountain were made of egg-shells. (Before long, the French press was speculating about "hollow mountains" that might be inhabited.) In a sense, Bouguer was right. What he did not realize was the reason for the mountain's "lightness": what underlies Chimborazo is a great block of light, granitic rock instead of the heavier basaltic rock normally found at that depth. In efforts to account for such anomalies, an English astronomer, George B. Airy, reasoned that mountains must have "roots" extending far down into the basaltic layer, and that a mountain of light density floats in the heavier rock as an iceberg floats in water. Out of such speculation the theory of isostasy was born and it is not hard to extend the theory from mountains to the continents themselves.

Wegener not only subscribed to the idea of buoyant continents supported in a denser medium but went on to insist that they were actually floating through this medium. Still, basalt is a dense, strong rock and all other scientists could make of Wegener's ideas was that he was proposing some mysterious force able to shove great, relatively fragile blocks of continental granite right through the basalt. They could conceive of no force on earth so powerful. Gradually, Wegener's ideas lost ground, only being resurrected from time to time by classroom instructors as the kind of glaring fallacy

This schematic drawing of a section of the earth shows how segments, or plates, of its crust are moved to carry continents around and cause deep earthquakes. The source of the movement is heat-caused currents within solid but plastic rock of the asthenosphere layer of the mantle. This rock melts when it nears the crust and oozes out through volcanoes (below) and through long splits or rifts, such as the one in the Mid-Atlantic Ridge (centre). Leaving the sea-bed rift, the molten rock forms fresh sea floor that spreads east and west, pushing ahead of it older crust sections, which may have continents on them. Where two such crust sections meet head-on, as they do in the trench off the coast of South America (below), the clash causes earthquakes. One section is pushed down into the mantle to be remelted, while the other is pushed up to form mountains—in this case, the Andes.

84

that even scientists could concoct when they paid too much attention to appearances and not enough to simple physics.

After World War II, new measuring techniques found their way into earth studies and began to produce provocative results. One device of the early '50s, the invention of British physicist P. M. S. Blackett, was the astatic magnetometer, an extremely sensitive instrument for measuring the amounts and directions of traces of magnetism. Geologists seized on it to detect the faint magnetism introduced into nearly all rocks by their content of iron granules. When ordinary rocks solidify out of magma, their iron granules freeze in the positions in which they had been aligned by the earth's magnetic field—like tiny compass needles. Using Blackett's magnetometer, British scientists discovered that the granules in the rocks of the British Isles were no longer lined up to point towards present-day magnetic poles but rather pointed some 30 degrees to one side. For a long time, scientists assumed that the earth's poles had moved—as they are known to do—and that the rocks' iron granules simply pointed to ancient positions of the poles. But later they found that the magnetic iron granules around the world often pointed towards widely different locations. Clearly, *something* had moved since the solidifying rocks froze their iron granules in place, but it became increasingly hard to believe that the poles had moved so frequently and so far.

OTHER new discoveries came in the 1950s, the most significant ones in the depths of the sea. Even though the oceans make up roughly three-quarters of the earth's surface, ocean-floor topography was then about as little known as Martian terrain is now. Scientists generally had based their theories about the earth on their knowledge of continents alone, a situation that, in the words of Maurice Ewing, the director of Columbia University's Lamont-Doherty Geological Observatory, "was about like trying to describe a football after being given a look at a piece of the lacing".

But after World War II, the U.S. Navy began to sponsor a gigantic programme to map all the world's ocean floors. The Navy's purpose was to chart the possible future battlegrounds for undersea warfare. As the maps emerged, they revealed an underwater topography that is in many ways far more striking than dry-land features. It was a terrain of endless abyssal plains, curious flat-topped sea mounts, submerged but active volcanoes, mysterious trenches and canyons. Most astonishing of all was the discovery that, if all the seas ran dry, the really dominant feature of our planet would be a vast mountain range whose extent first became obvious in 1958 on underwater maps based on studies by Columbia's Bruce C. Heezen and Marie Tharp. This 47,000-mile-long "mid-ocean ridge" weaves about the globe in more or less continuous curves like the long, single seam on a baseball. Unseen by seafarers on the surface thousands of feet above, its peaks project a mile or more above the ocean floor. Mariners are familiar with only a few peaks of the ridge, the great mountains that thrust high enough to be visible as islands. Iceland, the Azores, Ascensiot and Tristan de Cunha among others. The slopes of the ridge are steepest and most precipitous in the mid-Atlantic. There, broken into a jagged line by a number of fractures that cut straight across it like the lacings across the baseball seam, the ridge curves like steps so that it is precisely midway between the parallel S-shaped coastlines of the Old and New Worlds.

UNTIL the discovery of the mid-ocean ridge, scientists had been willing to dismiss the parallelism of the continental coastlines as mere coincidence, but the appearance of still another parallel feature strained coincidence too far; clearly a relationship of some kind existed between the Atlantic continents. As if to underline the lesson, the undersea maps revealed that the match between the opposing Atlantic shorelines was really far better than even Wegener had imagined. When one compared the edges of the continental shelves instead of the shorelines, the fit was practically perfect, not only between Africa and South America, but all the way north from the southern tips of these two continents to at least as far as Iceland.

Further discoveries about the ridge also seemed significant. For most of its length it was capped by a long slit, or rift—a slit that, along most of its length, was emitting heat and in some places was actually volcanic. A recent display of this volcanism is the new island of Surtsey, off the coast of Iceland. Surtsey, actually the top of a volcano in the ocean ridge system, first poked its head above water in 1963 and rose to 670 feet high and a mile and a half across. Quiescent, but still emitting heat and vapours, Surtsey already appears to have joined the world's inventory of habitable land: green plants have lodged on its shores, seals explore its beaches and sea birds nest on the side of its cone.

These discoveries virtually forced the reopening of the entire subject of moving continents, though geophysicists puzzled over what role the mid-ocean ridge and rift had in the scheme. To some the spectacle suggested that the earth had undergone a girth-splitting expansion. They viewed the ridge-rift system as simply a kind of scar tissue from the ancient expansion that had also broken up ancient proto-continents. The trouble with this idea was that the earth would have had to grow 3,000 miles wide just to open up the Atlantic Ocean, an amount of expansion that seemed physically impossible.

In 1961, another explanation was forthcoming. Princeton University geologist Harry Hess—until then a sceptic about continental drift—changed his mind. He wrote a paper called "Evolution of the Ocean Basin", an assemblage, modification and merging of old and new ideas that he labelled "geopoetry" because the ponderously fact-conscious earth sciences did not look kindly upon such pure hypothesizing. To account for the initial formation of continents, Hess adopted the "convection" theory as it had been developed by the Dutch geophysicist Felix A. Vening Meinisz. This accepts the modern view that the earth grew originally out of small particles of space dust, was heated up by the radioactivity of the material, and partially melted. Then, in a single, rather rapid turnover, the heavy elements among its components flowed as a molten mass to the centre, while lighter materials collected in several outer layers making up the mantle. Finally, a single topmost patch of light granitic material, like the froth on a kettle of soup, collected itself into continental material.

Hess then went on to accept continental drift as a present-day fact and, to account for it, borrowed and modified some little-known ideas and theories proposed a generation earlier by the British geologist Sir Arthur Holmes. Hess suggested that the mid-ocean ridge and its rift are indeed a kind of split in the earth's surface. But rather than being the result of expansion, they represent the place where hot mantle material is still coming up from the depths. Hess contended that the deep mantle is composed largely of a green gem-like material called olivine and that a current of olivine begins rising slowly upwards. As it nears the surface where temperature and pressure diminish, the olivine combines with water in the mantle, undergoing a change in crystalline make-up and becoming the greenish, marble-like rock called serpentine. Finally, the topmost portion of the serpentine actually melts as the pressure decreases, and flows out through cracks in the form of basalt lava. The basalt quickly freezes into a brittle crust riding on top of a somewhat less brittle layer of serpentine 50 to 100 miles thick. This serpentine layer, called the lithosphere, and its thin topping of basalt are continually forming at the mid-ocean ridge and then moving horizontally across the ocean to either side, cooling and growing heavier over millions of years. The ridge thus becomes a source of fresh ocean floor, supplying rock to a sort of conveyer belt that carries the new material away east and west. This same process can occur elsewhere on the earth, even in the basaltic layer under a continental block; then the conveyer belt breaks the continent apart and takes the pieces in opposite directions. This has happened on many occasions, beginning with the split that broke up the single original proto-continent, Hess believes. He also considers continental rifting and drifting an ongoing, present-day occurrence, the continents moving at the rate of an inch or so a year. In the Atlantic, for instance, the ocean floor conveyer belt apparently widens the sea at a rate of about an inch a year.

Parts of the Pacific floor appear to be moving faster than the Atlantic, and this fact may help to explain one of the puzzles that recent oceanographic studies turned up: the ocean floors are too clean. From what was already known about the rate of accumulation of sea-bed sediment—materials eroded from continents and dead organisms—the sediment layers on the deep ocean floors proved bafflingly thin. If they had been building up over the thousands of millions of years that oceans were thought to have existed, sediment ought to be miles deep in all the world's oceans. Instead, in most ocean regions, sediment depth rarely exceeds a few thousand feet and in some areas there is virtually no sediment at all. In fact, the sediment thickness varies widely from one ocean to another; the Pacific in particular has thinner layers than the Atlantic—possibly because the Pacific floor moves faster and is exposed for a shorter time to the gentle precipitation of sediment. Some scientists believe the fastest movement may be off the coast of Chile, where the ocean floor seems to slide under the South American continent at the rate of perhaps six inches a year.

Even this rate is hardly swift, but over the aeons it could account for tremendous changes in the earth. The Atlantic's one-inch-a-year movement would have been sufficient to create its entire 3,000-mile span in the comparatively brief time, geologically speaking, of about 200 million years. In comparison to the 4,500-million-year age of the earth, the Atlantic Ocean would be a newcomer. It would have begun to open up in the last stages of the age of dinosaurs.

If this indeed was the time when the earth's original single continent split apart, another puzzle might be solved. Each of the proto-continent's fragments could have carried with it a fair sample of the life forms then existing on land. Thus the same kinds of life would be spread all over the earth, to leave their remains in places now widely separated. Conceivably, the coal beds are in frozen Antarctica because, when coal was being formed from tropical forests, the antarctic land mass was situated in the tropics; almost identical fossil snails and earthworms turn up on the two sides of the Atlantic because, when those creatures evolved, South America and Africa were apparently part of one continent. But despite the elegant explanation that the new concept of "sea-floor spreading" provided for many perplexing discoveries, old and new, few earth scientists—especially in the U.S.—gave it much credence at first.

The theory of continental drift, as propounded by Alfred Wegener, held that all the continents originated as one huge land mass called Pangaea. Black lines show the outlines of present continents (1). Wegener theorized that various forces pulled Pangaea apart (2), gradually dispersing the continents towards their present positions (3). He cited the continents' jigsaw-puzzle effect as well as fossil and glacial evidence to support his hypothesis.

THE most persuasive way of proving a new theory in science is to use it to predict some hitherto unobserved consequence that would be hard to account for in any other way. In 1963, a 23-year-old English graduate student named Frederick Vine first proposed just such a classic test of sea-floor spreading. Vine had been a continental drift convert from the age of fourteen, when he had been fascinated by the same coastline similarity that had tantalized such men as Bacon and Wegener. He was aware of the then new discovery that from time to time, usually at intervals of hundreds of thousands of years, the earth has reversed its magnetic field, switching the North Pole to the South Pole. If hot mantle material was extruded from the crest of the mid-ocean ridge in the way Hess suggested, Vine reasoned, its iron granules should show those pole reversals. Some granules should point one way, some another. The rock in the mantle would thus be imprinted by stripes of alternating magnetic polarity running parallel to the mid-ocean ridge. In effect, the ocean-floor basalt should be recording earth's ancient magnetic history like the tape in a mammoth recorder. Soon after Vine had published his idea, a magnetic survey of the sea floor near Iceland disclosed just such a zebra-like pattern of stripes straddling the Mid-Atlantic Ridge.

The second classic test of ocean-floor spreading was made by Lynn Sykes of the Lamont-Doherty Geological Observatory. By studying the earthquake motions caused by fractures across the mid-ocean ridge, he proved that the sea floors on both sides of the ridge have been spreading away from it.

Vine's and Sykes's proofs have now been supplemented by an array of other evidence. In 1968, for instance, a number of U.S. oceanographic and geological institutions sent out a specially equipped ship, the *Glomar Challenger*, to extract sea-bed cores from depths previously unreachable. The *Glomar Challenger* was fitted with newly developed apparatus for deep-sea drilling that provided "dynamic positioning"; sonar beams and engine power maintained the unanchored ship in an exact position despite the winds, currents and heaving seas of mid-ocean. Anchoring in mid-ocean would have been out of the question: even if the several miles of anchor cables did not break under the strain of their own weight, they would have far too much slack to permit drilling operations. The ship, crew and rotating teams of scientists began a series of voyages in all the world's oceans, drilling through ocean sediments lying as far as 20,000 feet down and into the underlying mantle. On one of their very first penetrations they discovered traces of oil in the bottom of the Gulf of Mexico, some 12,000 feet down. This is far below the level at which conventional theories would predict that oil could be formed and the implications of the find are still not clear to geologists.

But even more important, the deep-sea drilling added new confirmation and new detail to the picture of spreading ocean floors. An obvious prediction based upon the theory is that the basalt at the mid-ocean ridge must be much younger than the basalt near the continental margins. For this reason, the ocean floor near the ridge should have collected a thinner layer of sediment. Extracting sample cores of sediment across the Atlantic, the *Glomar Challenger* expedition found not only that the layer of sediment got thinner as they approached the ridge, but also that the lowest sediment lying just on top of the basalt floor was younger nearer the ridge. (The sediment's age can be estimated from the kinds of fossil skeletons of marine organisms embedded in the sample.)

THE abundance of confirming evidence from studies such as that conducted by the *Glomar Challenger* team has by now convinced most scientists that the sea floors are spreading. But they are far from agreeing as to what makes it happen. Hess had proposed that the driving energy was heat from radioactivity in the mantle. This resulted in "convection"—the rising and falling circulation patterns that also occur in a boiling kettle of soup or in the air above a radiator. In the hot but hard solid rock of the mantle, this circulation manifests itself as plastic flowing, the pace of which —an inch or so a year—is imperceptibly slow in human terms, though in geological terms quite significant. Even so, accustomed as we are to the view of rock as the very symbol of solidity, the notion of a flowing earth wrenches the intuitions of most laymen, just as it did those of many geophysicists themselves. The people who talk of convection currents describe the mantle as having about the same consistency as another seemingly rigid material that, like rock, can flow plastically—high-quality steel like that in jet turbine blades. Turbine blades, for example, slowly lengthen during many hours of operation; the jet engine must be rebuilt before they finally begin scraping the turbine walls. But a more appropriate analogue for mantle consistency would be the well-known play material, "Silly Putty", which fractures under sudden blows but flows quite readily under the gentle pressure of its own weight. The outer crust, however, is much more brittle than the mantle.

Even among those who agree that convection is responsible for sea-floor spreading, many differences of opinion exist over how deep the convection extends and how far around the earth the closed "cells" or complete loops of rising and falling currents extend. A large number of scientists distrust the convection explanation entirely, doubting that the forces involved are powerful enough. Some prefer the explanation that the crust is actually sliding down the slopes of the ridge under the pull of gravity. They believe the ridge itself was pushed up when highly compressed mantle material expanded through a weak area in the overlying crust. The expansion is caused by a change in crystalline structure that incorporates into the rock some water naturally present in the mantle. Many authorities believe it is the transport of water to the surface in this way that has filled the oceans.

After the idea of sea-floor spreading was accepted, an obvious implication remained to be explained away: if new surface area keeps being formed while the size of the earth stays the same, somehow as much crustal material must get destroyed as gets created. Hess and Holmes had suggested rather vaguely that perhaps all the new crust disappeared under continents being melted or absorbed.

How the crust might be consumed became clear from the studies of Japanese and American seismologists who were investigating the earthquakes of the mysterious "island arcs" (Japan, the Aleutians and the Marianas). These numerous, similarly shaped archipelagos have long tantalized geographers and geophysicists. All the roughly bow-shaped chains of islands are of volcanic origin—collectively they are called the Pacific ring of fire —and, in fact, most can be regarded simply as the tips of huge volcanoes that have piled up until they finally projected their snouts above water. And each arc parallels a deep ocean trench. The seismologists, after locating the exact points of origin, or foci, of the earthquakes at each arc-trench combination, found that most of the foci fitted into a pattern. They form a kind of long, sloping plane with one end near the bottom of the arc's trench. From there, the plane slants down at an angle of about 45 degrees, reaching deep into the earth's interior and passing underneath the islands of the arc. Some quake foci were detected as deep as 450 miles into the earth's interior. These seismological "X-rays" of events in the mantle suggested the ultimate fate of the sea-floor conveyer belts; at a trench two sections of crust moving in opposite directions meet head-on; one is overridden by another and is bent downwards to be sent plunging at a 45-degree angle back into the mantle from which it emerged originally. All the strains of bending, cracking, scraping and ultimately melting suffered by the crust as it plunges into the hot interior are the source of island-arc earthquakes.

As they study the locations of ridges, trenches and faults, together with the directions of sea-floor movement as revealed by magnetic stripes, scientists have begun to discern that the earth's crust is an array of separately moving plates. Taken together, these plates completely cover the earth. There are roughly half a dozen major crustal plates, most of which have entire continents embedded in them like logs trapped in ice. There are, in addition, a larger number of minor plates. Generally speaking, each plate is outlined along one edge by the rift in the mid-ocean ridge, along another edge by a trench, and along the remaining edges by fault lines, regions where the differently moving plates grind against each other. "Sea-floor spreading", which supplanted "continental drift", has in turn given way to the even more catchy concept "plate tectonics" ("tectonics" being the geological term for any process by which land features are formed). And the theory of plate tectonics is now often referred to as "the new global tectonics", for, as will be related in later chapters, the revolutionary new discovery appears finally to account for much of the scrambled, hitherto inexplicable, physiognomy of Mother Earth.

NEARLY TWO MILES UNDERGROUND, AFRICAN GOLD-MINERS TRUDGE ALONG A TUNNEL IN ROBINSON DEEP MINE, JOHANNESBURG

The Great Treasure Hunt

Alone among all the earth's creatures, man learned to dig its treasures to make tools. Stone Age men scratched for flint, and their more knowing descendants mined their way through the Bronze and Iron Ages. The earth's coal fired the Industrial Revolution; now its uranium fuels the nuclear age. And its most dazzling prizes are the same today as they have always been: diamonds and gold.

91

A MONSTER DIGGER, reaching 420 feet from shovel to chute, excavates rock covering an Illinois coal strip. After it clears this overlayer, other machines scoop coal from the exposed surface.

GRINDING AWAY at the face of a rich coal seam, this mechanical miner cuts out a ton every 30 seconds. Machinery in its wake gathers the broken coal, conveys it back to a shaft and hoists it to the surface. In the past two decades machines have tripled the rate of coal production in the U.S.A.; most miners there now operate machines instead of swinging picks.

Coal: Ammunition for a Revolution

Ever since it started to turn the wheels and forge the steel of the new industrial order 200 years ago, coal has been man's primary source of power. Long before, the Roman armies had used it for their camp fires, "mining" it simply by digging shallow holes into visible outcroppings. Today machines have taken over much of the hard digging, both on the surface and far underground. There is a lot of coal there. For example, a tenth of the area of the U.S.A. is underlaid by coal, and most of the original reserve of nearly two million million tons is still untapped.

The creation of this storehouse of potential energy goes back about 345 million years to the time when vast swampy areas of the earth were covered by dense, sun-drenched plant forests. As the plants died in the marshes, crustal disturbances occurred. Shallow seas and layers of sediments inundated the forests, and later new swamps grew in their place. In some areas this alternation of swamp and sea occurred hundreds of times. Slowly, great pressures and ample time worked chemical changes, hardening and fossilizing the layers of decayed vegetation. The result was seams of coal, still rich in the solar energy absorbed by the plants so long ago.

CLEARING AWAY coal which they have blasted from the face of a narrow vein, these Kentucky miners, their backs bent to the low ceiling, still strain to the shovel as their grandfathers did. In the United States, such laborious pick-and-shovel mining is now confined mostly to abandoned mines or else outcroppings being reworked by individuals.

SOUTH AFRICAN MINERS DIG FOR DIAMONDS AMONG THE EROSION-ROUNDED ROCKS OF AN ALLUVIAL DEPOSIT NORTH OF KIMBERLEY

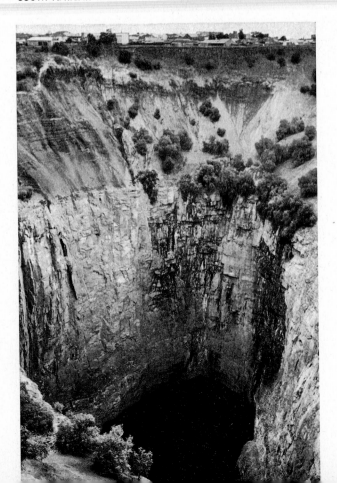

Diamonds, Born in the Depths

Few substances look less alike than coal and diamond, yet both are fashioned from the same elemental carbon. No one knows exactly what goes on deep in the earth where the startling change from soft carbon to hard crystal is made. But to form diamonds, experiments show that carbonaceous material must be subjected to temperatures of at least 2,800° C. and to pressures of over a million pounds per square inch. It is reckoned that these conditions must prevail at some points 240 miles down in the earth's interior. Once formed, diamonds are carried to the surface by molten magma during volcanic eruptions. When it cools, a plug in the crust remains, called a diamond pipe. Within the pipe is a mass of

THE "BIG HOLE", an abandoned mine in Kimberley, shows the shaft-like shape of a diamond pipe. It produced over £90 million worth of diamonds in 26 years.

GEM STONES VALUED AT MORE THAN A QUARTER OF A MILLION POUNDS SPARKLE IN A FRYING-PAN AFTER BEING WASHED IN AN ACID BATH

bluish rock known as kimberlite, which is seeded with diamonds.

Long before the discovery of such pipes near Kimberley, South Africa, in the 1870s, miners in India and Brazil had been digging up diamonds scattered in dried-up river beds. These deposits were left by running water which picked up diamonds from volcanic pipes and dropped them miles away. Africa is rich in such alluvial beds as well as in pipe mines, and now produces 97 per cent of the world's annual diamond output of about 22 million carats, or about four tons. About 80 per cent are used industrially, since diamond, the earth's hardest material, is a useful tool as well as an ornament to beauty.

INDUSTRIAL DIAMONDS are mined in great quantity in the Congo. These stones will be used in abrasives and for drilling everything from teeth to oil wells.

The Bright Lure of Gold

Because it is rare, very beautiful, easily worked and never tarnishes, gold has always been the earth's most prized element. The Egyptians, first to mine it, considered it the "royal metal". Medieval alchemists strove to turn base metals into gold, a frustrated dream that was nevertheless the cause of many of the early advances in chemistry. Europe's lust for it helped to launch the voyages of exploration that opened the New World. Modern economists regard gold as "global money", the only totally acceptable medium of international exchange.

So thorough has been the search for gold that the days are gone when it could be panned commercially from the beds of streams, and a nugget weighing 208 (troy weight) pounds could turn up in a wagon rut, as happened in Australia. Now men must burrow deep for gold, and South African miners, like the sweating man on the left, have already blasted through rock to a depth of over two miles. For all the time, energy and lives spent in pursuit of gold, the amount taken from the earth seems pitifully small. It has been estimated that if world gold production from 1943 to 1955—a period encompassing the greatest strikes in Latin America, California, Australia, South Africa and Alaska—were melted down, it would bulk only as large as a 50-foot cube. Its value, however, at today's official rate would be more than £30,000 million.

A PROUD MINER, a migrant from Portuguese East Africa, labours in Johannesburg's Robinson Deep gold-mine. Nearly depleted, the mine has produced more than 13 million ounces of gold in 68 years.

AN ARRAY OF GOLD shows the basic types mined (*opposite*). The rough is lode gold, found with quartz at depth; the smooth nuggets come from surface mines. The American $20 coin dates from 1855.

URANIUM-RICH VEIN of the yellowish mineral carnotite is tested by a prospector with a Geiger-counter. Found mostly in the Colorado Plateau, carnotite is one of the main sources of uranium in the U.S.A. Before the nuclear age made uranium an element of prime importance, carnotite had only a modest value as a source of radium and vanadium.

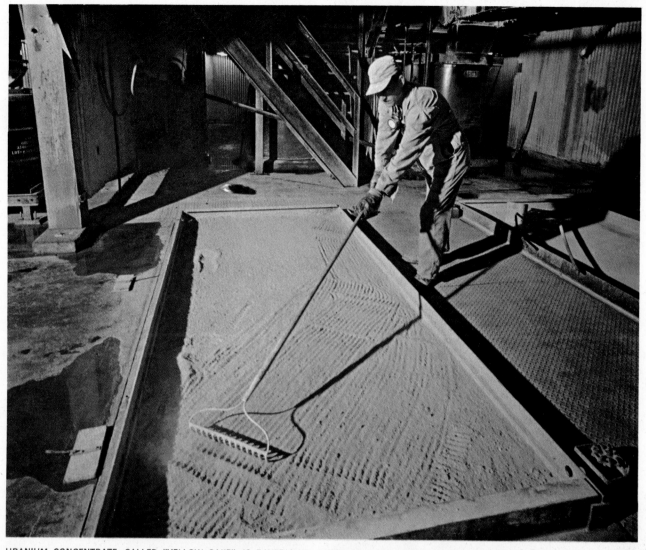

URANIUM CONCENTRATE, CALLED "YELLOW CAKE", IS RAKED AND DRIED AT A MILL. ITS YELLOW COLOUR IS LOST DURING REFINING

Precious Metal of a New Age

With the explosion of the first atomic bomb over the New Mexico desert in 1945, uranium—the basic ingredient of nuclear power and weapons— suddenly became the most sought-after metal of the nuclear age. As metals go, it is neither very rare nor particularly glamorous. Because it never occurs in a pure state, and seldom in heavy concentration, vast amounts of ore must be found, mined and refined, in a long, costly process, to produce small quantities of the final product (*right*). But the world's nuclear powers have created an urgent demand for it. Deposits of rich ore, such as those in the Congo, Romania, Canada and the U.S.A., are being intensively mined, while a world-wide search for more continues.

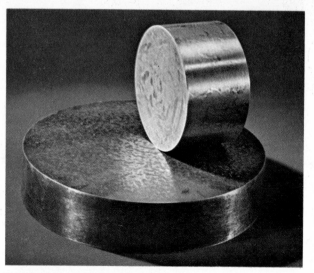

ELEMENTAL URANIUM, a heavy grey metal, is the basic source of fuel for nuclear reactors. Because of its strategic importance, all uranium is under governmental control.

99

PYRITE, QUARTZ

YELLOW WULFENITE

PEACOCK COAL

MICROCLINE, SMOKY QUARTZ

BOTRYOIDAL AZURITE, MALACHITE, LIMONITE

CHRYSOTILE (ASBESTOS)

The Glittering Faces
of Earth's Rocks and Minerals

Apart from providing the raw stuff of civilization's tools, the rocks which make up the crust of the earth have fascinated man throughout the ages simply by their natural beauty and extraordinary variety. Today in the United States there are over two million enthusiastic amateurs who are captivated

VARISCITE

PELE'S HAIR

GARNET

AMETHYST

RUBY SPHALERITE

CHALCANTHITE

by the lure of collecting strange and arresting specimens of the earth's remarkable alchemy. Altogether there are just under 2,000 different minerals in the crust and they present a bewildering and dazzling assortment of colours, shapes and textures. On these pages is a collection of rocks and minerals with striking contrasts. They range from the fragile, spun-glass effect of Pele's hair to the iridescent sheen of an ordinary lump of peacock coal, and from the rough fibres of natural asbestos to the brilliance of ruby sphalerite, which looks just like—but is not—a priceless gem.

ORDINARY LIGHT shows a nondescript collection of mineral-bearing rocks as they naturally appear. Only the trained eye can detect the characteristics that distinguish them.

ULTRA-VIOLET LIGHT produces an array of distinctive luminescence in the same pile of rocks. Fluorite gives off a blue glow, calcite a red, willemite green and scapolite yellow.

A Weird Ultra-violet World

In the light of day not all minerals have the vivid beauty of those on the preceding pages. Many look drably alike, and to differentiate between them there are tests for such physical properties as texture, hardness and specific gravity. But a more spectacular test, involving the use of ultra-violet light, can turn even the dullest minerals into rainbows of ghostly colour. The short wavelengths of ultra-violet light make it invisible to the human eye, but they produce in the crystals of some minerals an impulse which gives off energy in the form of longer-waved, visible light. This property, known as "luminescence", is inherent in certain minerals and absent in others. Thus, though impurities and differences in crystal structure can complicate the tests, exposure to ultra-violet light is a valuable guide to a mineral's identification. This test has been used extensively both in the laboratory and in the field in prospecting for uranium, zinc and tungsten.

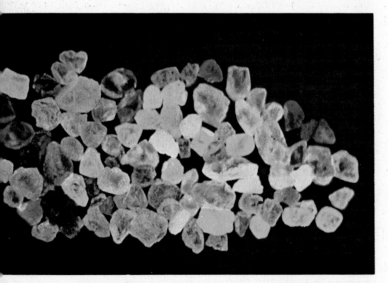

ODD DIAMONDS, otherwise normal, respond to ultra-violet light with a display of colour. Only one gem diamond in 100 shows such colour variation, instead of a blue-white light.

PURE SCHEELITE, a primary ore of tungsten, identifies itself with a display of blue hues. An all-white or a yellow tint would show that molybdenum was also present in the ore.

A GREEN GLOW is emitted under ultra-violet light by willemite, a zinc mineral. The red glow comes from calcite. The commercial value of luminescence was first realized accidentally in 1905 by mine workers in Franklin, New Jersey, who found that willemite dust glowed distinctively when exposed to electric sparks from milling machinery.

5

Shaping the Landscape

I‍T is not every day that a new-born volcano shoots lava out of a cornfield, or an island sinks beneath the waves, or an earthquake crumbles a city. While the earth is always rearranging its features, most of its changes of face are leisurely rather than catastrophic. A human lifetime simply does not offer a long enough look to make the changes apparent. So until a few generations ago it was reasonable to assume, and most people did, that landscape was here to stay, pending the Last Judgement. That the hills were eternal or at least, as William Cullen Bryant put it, "ancient as the sun", was generally unquestioned.

But 19th-century geologists were already taking closer looks at the earth around them and beginning to find clues that had been available all the time. Shorelines were everywhere advancing or in retreat: Niagara's brink was receding a few feet every year; some "eternal" hills were decaying while others appeared to be rising. In time it was realized that even the splash of a single raindrop on the soil, imperceptible to man although overwhelming to a mite or wood-louse, counted for something in the remoulding of the earth. In the course of this reappraisal of landscape, the ruins of the

Greek temple of Serapis at Pozzuoll, near Naples, became a sort of geologic Exhibit A. When this building was excavated and studied by scientists, it was found that several of its columns were still standing upright,
and that three of them were riddled with holes drilled by a species of borer
clam that is still common in the near-by Mediterranean. What was puzzling
was that some of these holes were bored near the tops of the columns, there
being no known way that clams could have climbed up there. The mystery
was not settled until men could bring themselves to believe what the evidence so clearly showed: the temple, some time after its construction, had
been engulfed by the sea when the land under it sank; later on it rose again,
its columns still upright.

Nothing else on the face of the globe, it turns out, is immutable either.
Not only are volcanoes and mountains being shoved up and ground away,
but seas open and close, new continents form, old ones get bigger or split
apart. Our topography, our climate and our mineral resources are all consequences of this turmoil. The two major influences at work are, on the
one hand, the crust-moving forces of global tectonics that raise land and
mountains above the sea. On the other hand are the forces of weathering
and erosion, whose constant nibbling tears things down again.

IN so far as the parochial interests of man are concerned, the most important contribution of the tectonic process has been the creation of the
dry land upon which he lives. The process by which continents are formed
resembles nothing quite so much as the events that take place in a sim-
mering kettle of soup. Like froth on broth, the continents always seem to
stay afloat, despite the way their underlying plates of basaltic rock emerge
and descend. Not only are several existing continents growing larger or higher by having new material added, but some new continents may be in the
process of being born. Most of the new growth and birth activity is centred near the island arcs and deep trenches of the Pacific. The island chains
are now assumed to be either infant continents themselves or emergent
additions to the near-by Asian continent. For one thing, a common island
rock is one called andesite. Andesite was named after the Andes Mountains,
on top of which it was found, and the coincidence of its occurrence in such
different places leads to the conclusion that the islands and the infant Andes
must have been formed originally by similar processes.

According to this view, the mantle underlying these trenches is the caul-
dron that concocts the light granite of continental rock. As a moving plate
of the crust's heavy basalt slides in from seaward and plunges into a trench,
the basalt and its sediment layer dip into the hot mantle and melt. Mixed
with some sea water that has also been carried down, the basalt-sediment
combination is transformed by heat and sea salt into a molten precursor of
continental granite. Under pressure this mixture surges up through cracks
in the overlying crustal plate, creating volcanoes that eventually poke their
heads above water as islands. Geologists believe they have found remnants
of such island arcs in the heartlands of several continents, one example being
the North American continent's Canadian Shield region. Continents grow
outwards from these volcanic nuclei as new sediment—and perhaps even
other continents—is carried in by ocean-floor conveyer belts.

During this growing process, the continental surfaces may crumple upwards to form mountain ranges. The western mountains of the U.S., for in-

stance, are probably the old edge of a continent that rode over a trench and buckled under the conflicting stresses from the westward-pressing forces of the Atlantic ridge and eastward-pressing forces of the Pacific ridge. Other mountains, such as the Andes, are continuing to grow because a fast-moving (six inches a year) crustal plate from the Pacific is plunging under the South American continent at a trench off the coast of Chile.

An even more violent event is assumed to account for the soaring Himalayas, the world's highest mountains. Most scientists now believe that at one time India was a separate continent, riding on an ocean plate that moved northwards and plunged under the then-existing Asian land mass. India jammed against Asia and stopped moving, though not until India itself was partially wedged under Asia, creating the double-thickness region that we see as the Himalayas.

THE moving plates of the earth also tear continents apart. The long Gulf of California represents the beginning of a split in the American continent along the same seam that forms the earthquake-prone San Andreas fault near Los Angeles. Here a strip of coastal territory in Mexico and California is being wrenched and ripped northwards, probably as a consequence of unbalanced forces set up ages ago when the continent was pushed bodily over part of the mid-ocean ridge system in the Pacific. The Red Sea is the long narrow gulf between Asia and Africa that was created when a fork of the mid-ocean ridge left the Indian Ocean and snaked its way inland. Recently it has been suggested that the Biblical account of Moses leading the Israelites across the momentarily dry Red Sea floor may really refer to some turbulent activity in the rift that temporarily emptied the Red Sea. While the continents are splitting apart, their mountains are being whittled down by various agents of erosion. Erosion by itself would wash most of North America into the oceans within 25 million years, leaving only a wide, low plain. The greatest of the agents of erosion is running water. We have noted that the atmosphere sucks up about 100,000 cubic miles of moisture a year. Most of this falls back into the oceans, but about 35,000 cubic miles of it reaches the land as rain, snow, sleet, hail and dew. A great deal of the precipitation goes underground and a great deal more evaporates again before flowing very far, but an estimated 10,000 million million gallons runs off to replenish the seas. This is the flood that year after year is the paramount instrument in shaping the land.

It is not so much the water itself that acts as the sculptor but rather the particles and chemicals that it carries along. The change in colour from clear, swift mountain stream to the brown, placid currents of a major river shows how each tributary adds its portion of particles to the main stream's load. The Mississippi river system, for example, drains an area of about a million and a quarter square miles. In a year, something like 600 million tons of mud, clay, mineral fragments and pinpoint-sized lumps of raw rock, all torn from the drainage area of tributary streams, are carried down to be added to the Gulf of Mexico's burden of accumulating sediments. From the first bright flake of mica swirling in a mountain brook to the last quartz sand grain stripped from a downstream bar, each particle serves as one of the Mississippi system's erosive teeth, nibbling at river banks and beds along the way.

The speed of water flow is a vital factor in the erosive power of streams.

A youthful, steep mountain torrent, flowing about 10 feet a second, not only carries fine particles in suspension and mineral salts in solution, but also rolls, pushes and tumbles masses of pebbles, gravel and even boulders downhill along its bed. As the gradient levels off and the water loses speed, the larger stones are left behind, then the smaller ones. A stream is a kind of sorting machine, grading its suspended load with fair precision. Coarse materials fall out first, gravels and sands reaching the bottom and the banks long before the finer fragments of mud can sink. It is this mechanism that provided the deposits of gold, tin and platinum that were exploited by placer mining; these heavy metals, tumbling down from water-worn ore deposits in the mountains, were often concentrated by the sorting action of running water. Similarly, when a rapid-running stream leaves the confines of a canyon, it changes its rate of flow as it runs out on to the flat and deposits an alluvial fan of well-sorted material, the coarser fragments lying nearest the canyon and the finer ones on the outer fringes of the fan.

STREAMS run; glaciers merely crawl; yet flowing ice is a spectacular agent of erosion. A glacier is an accumulation of snow gradually compressed into ice. Eventually its weight gets so immense that it begins to slide downhill, gouging the bedrock in its path with stones and boulders embedded in its bottom and bulldozing soil and whatever else may be in the way. But a river goes as far in a few seconds as an average glacier does in a year. Many glaciers in the Alps creep downhill only a foot a day; some in Alaska advance as much as 40 feet.

The lack of speed is no indication of a glacier's effectiveness in sculpting topography. A glacier 1,000 feet thick exerts a force of nearly 30 tons on each square foot on the valley floor underneath it, and the pressure enables the stones dragged along by the glacier to scour and polish the bedrock below. Valleys are not actually begun by glaciers, but glacial erosion remodels the contours left by running water. The result is a U-shaped valley with a broad, flat floor and steep sides, strewn with rock debris deposited as the glacier recedes.

The world's only ice caps today, covering Greenland and Antarctica, and the ice sheets that repeatedly spread over other continents in the past, have abraded landscapes much as mountain glaciers do, but on a vaster scale. Ice caps spread radially, scraping up all loose or protuberant material below them. The Laurentide ice sheet that once ground its way down over North America stripped much of Canada to bedrock, leaving innumerable shallow depressions now filled by lakes, and a denuded land that even today can barely support vegetation. Just as Scandinavia is thought to be still rebounding from the depressing weight of its most recent burial in the ice, parts of North America are still recovering from their Laurentide entombment. The ice sheet reached as far as St. Louis in the Mid-West and New York City in the East, forcing the earth's crust downwards as much as 1,000 feet and transferring southwards the Northlands' ancient beds of fertile soil.

The great ice sheets did more than transport the soil. Through centuries of ice advance and retreat, their forward edges bulged with outwash, partly a flour-fine mud made up of so-called "unweathered" materials. It contained fragments of quartz, feldspar, mica and calcite, planed from the bedrock. This gritty mud soon dried. Then the wild winds of the ice-age took command, and swept the dry powder away in dust storms such as the world has never seen since. Today, from the Caspian through the plains of Central Asia to the basin of the Hwang Ho in China, and from the Rockies to western Pennsylvania in the United States, there are deposits up to hundreds of feet deep of the rich loam known as "loess". It is composed of particles of the very rock dust that the ice-sheets released to the winds. It is remarkable stuff: it may be carved with a knife, and caves dozens of feet high can be excavated from it. Roads that run through loess deposits grow more deeply rutted each season. In China, after years of use, they lie as much as 40 feet below the surface of the tilled land on either side.

The far-flung loess deposits show what wind can do to pile up eroded materials, but this should not permit an over-emphasis on the wind itself as an eroding force. Not very long ago, as geological theories go, the weirdly balanced rocks, arches, natural bridges, spires and pinnacles of desert areas were all ascribed to wind—or aeolian—erosion. Now geologists know that water was the principal destructive agent, for wind must carry sand before it can cut, and even a strong wind cannot lift sand above tombstone height. Fine dust can be lifted much higher, but it is powerless to erode.

Natural arches and pinnacles often owe their bizarre shapes to mechanical weathering, a process which is noticeable in desert areas and which is accentuated by dry climate and wide variations in temperature. Sunlight plays a part in it: the dark-coloured mineral grains in a granite block heat up faster than the lighter ones, and their different expansion rates bring on stresses that crumble the surface into a mass of loose crystals. Water, freezing in rock cracks and crevices, does more. It expands 10 per cent when it freezes, acting like a crow-bar in forcing the cracks apart. Similarly, in forest areas plant and tree roots do the same thing, penetrating the soil-filled fissures and splitting the rock simply by growing.

Much weathering goes on underground. The raindrops that the earth soaks up fill the interstices between soil and sand particles, penetrate the pores of the porous rocks, and generally invade the crust to a depth of some hundreds of thousands of feet. They contribute to the water table, which is the upper surface of a more or less saturated zone that roughly follows the landscape contours. The water table appears above ground as lakes and ponds, trickles out in hillside springs or seeps in the hollows, and fills the lower portions of wells or gushes up from artesian bores.

There is probably more water underground at any one time than in all the lakes and rivers combined. This underground water leaches chemical compounds out of one formation, to deposit them in another. When the water carries enough carbonic acid—from dissolved atmospheric carbon dioxide and decayed organic material—and when it percolates through limestone formations, chemical weathering occurs. The acid eats away the rock, and the water becomes filled with dissolved limestone in the form of a calcium-carbonate solution. In limestone flats the ground may collapse, producing the pits called swallow-holes in England, karsts in Europe, *cenotes* in Yucatán, sink-holes in Florida, Virginia, Tennessee and Kentucky, and blamed nuisances in Indiana, where there may be hundreds of them in one square mile.

The same percolation has hollowed out such earth cavities as Luray Cave in Virginia, Mammoth Cave in Kentucky, and the all-but-endless Carlsbad Caverns of New Mexico, with their surrealistic arrays of stalactites and stalagmites, columns and solid rock veils, all made of

The sketch above illustrates how caves are cut in layers of limestone. Water containing carbonic acid seeps down through fissures in the ground (A and B) and, stopped by a layer of more resistant rock, eats its way laterally through the limestone until it reaches the river (C).

In this sketch chemical weathering of the cave has continued until fissure B becomes a swallow-hole and the acidic water has managed to penetrate an underlying layer of shale. Meanwhile erosion has deepened the river and lowered its water-level, leaving the original cave dry except for seepage.

calcium carbonate precipitated, drop by drop, as dripstone. There are many minerals, for that matter, such as those in the ferro-magnesium group, which originate deep in the earth and are unstable under surface conditions. The red and brown stains on rocks containing them are signs of their chemical decay under attack by carbonic acid and atmospheric oxygen.

Weathering can be considered to be the basic process on which all erosion rests, for it produces the first crumbled bits of rock, which are later used by water and wind to do their abrading work. Its importance to man is obvious, for it provides the chief ingredient for soil—without which the continents would be lifeless. Soil, although it also contains decayed organic matter, consists mostly of mineral grains—those transient fragments of rock dust which constitute the soil of the continents, and whose destiny, in the distant future, is to be compressed into rock once again. The grit that makes up soil is an ideal medium for the activity of plant growth. Plants must have access to nitrogen in soluble form, being unable to absorb it directly from the air. They get it in two ways: lightning converts it into oxides which rain washes into the soil, and certain bacteria in the soil convert it from gas into compounds which the plants can assimilate. The humus, the earth-worm castings and other animal excretions present in soil also act as reservoirs of soluble nitrogen. The nitrogen cycle is vital to life, and the weathered rock in the soil is vital to the perpetuation of the cycle.

At the outset of this chapter we saw that the sea plays at least a bystanding role in the diastrophic rising and sinking of shores. It is also an agent of erosion. Each year, every coastline on earth pays tribute to the tides and the wind-propelled waves in the form of coarse and fine debris that is pulled down to the sediment beds of the continental shelves. Yet the ocean can add to the landscape as well as take it away. The great sandspit called Cape Cod, in Massachusetts, is being steadily devoured along the front that its Great Beach presents to the Atlantic, but is being steadily rebuilt with sand formations that bend round into sheltered Cape Cod Bay. The great off-shore sandbars that culminate in Cape Hatteras in Carolina, and which provided the Wright brothers with good gliding terrain at Kitty Hawk, were all built up by the sea from materials borrowed from the North Carolina lands that lie inland from Albemarle and Pamlico Sounds.

But the sea's prime function in the erosion cycle is to serve as a repository, a dumping-ground for all the wastes of the land. It is the grave where all the pulverized continents would be interred if nothing ever restrained erosion. Its mineral salts, including sodium chloride, are a great, well-stirred accumulation of material dissolved out of rocks. Its floor is an even greater accumulation of the sediments of earth. These are deposited in various ways. Undertow sucks sand, gravel and clay out from the shore. In some areas the shells of living organisms are abundant enough, as in the case of coral, to become important deposits. When sea water becomes locally supersaturated with certain salts, like calcium carbonate, they are precipitated out and form deposits on the bottom.

The build-up of deposits may cover the floors of such shallow extensions of the ocean as Hudson Bay and the Baltic, but elsewhere it is concentrated on the continental shelves, spilling down the slope to depths of two or three thousand feet. Not much sediment from the land actually gets to the deepest ocean beds. But at river deltas, most of which are underneath the water, tremendous burdens of sediments are borne by the sea floor and the underlying crust. The Piedmont district of Italy is a great alluvial plain composed of such stream-deposits, and a similar plain stretches out from the western edge of the Sierra Nevada range in the United States. Nearly every river has a delta, except where the sea is deep or turbulent. The Mississippi's mud delta by now is perhaps 30,000 feet thick and nobody knows exactly how heavy. Some geologists think that parts of the gulf floor keep sinking as more sediment piles up. Others say that the floor is sinking by itself, and that the silt and debris from the Mississippi do not affect it.

As younger sediment deposits bury older ones, the latter are gradually compressed into solid rock. Gravel beds become conglomerate, sand becomes sandstone, clayey mud becomes shale, and calcite slimes turn into limestone. Even though most sediments end up in the ocean, the periodic upheavals of the crust, and the changes of sea-level during ice-ages and thaws, have succeeded in leaving sedimentary rocks almost everywhere. About 80 per cent of the earth's surface is sheathed in them, though by far the greater part of the crust still consists of igneous rock. Each major sedimentary rock has its own rate of deposition, an arbitrary measure based on the length of time it takes to build up a layer a foot thick. Although these rates can be estimated, they vary widely for each rock, depending on how favourable local conditions are. Shale, the most abundant sedimentary rock on the continents, has the fastest rate: 1,000 years a foot, while limestone averages some 6,000 years. Limestone takes longer because it originates with materials that come from the shells and skeletons of aquatic life, which are not so plentiful a source of sediment as are rivers and streams.

By a well-informed reading of the events embodied in the sheath of sedimentary deposits, the geologist can unravel much of the history of erosion versus diastrophism. A limestone layer, whatever its present elevation above sea-level, suggests that the region once formed the bed of a sea in which the ancestors of clams and snails lived. A seam of coal betrays an ancient swamp whose rich vegetation was partly decomposed when it was inundated by water and buried under later rock. A layer of salt or gypsum points to a body of salt water that later ebbed or dried up.

Sometimes the layers are all mixed up and the history takes a little deciphering. One series of sedimentary layers may lie at an angle below the surface, and another series may lie horizontally above it. This is called an "unconformity", and is good evidence that three geological processes occurred there in a definite sequence. First, existing beds of sediment were uplifted, tilted, and left above sea-level by crustal movements. Secondly, erosion worked away at the uplifted strata until they were worn flat, and thirdly, the region finally sank again below sea-level to permit more sediments to be deposited on top of them.

Studying the time-consuming sequences of mountain-building, erosion, sediment deposit and later uplifting has been the main concern of geologists for the past century. Collaborating in the detective work have been another group of earth scientists, the palaeontologists, or fossil hunters. Probing in the same sedimentary beds, they have found all sorts of traces, faint and plain, of the early forms of life on earth, sorting them out in sequence according to the rocks' relative ages and thereby giving the students of evolution their most useful evidence. The grand tableau that has been recon-

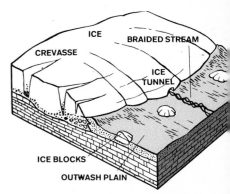

In this drawing of a glacial front, the glacier, riven by crevasses, has reached a point where it melts faster than its ice is advancing. In front of it is the outwash plain, composed of silt washed down by the melting of the ice. Through the plain flows a braided stream of ice-water issuing from a tunnel within the glacial ice. Buried in the plain are massive iceblocks left behind as the glacier receded.

This sketch shows the same area after the glacier's retreat. The most striking feature is the moraine, a ridge made of soil and rock carried downhill by the glacier and deposited. Drumlins may also be made in this way. The esker is made of gravel left behind by the glacial stream. A depression made by the glacier's weight has become a lake, while the holes in the plain, called kettles, formed as the ice-blocks melted.

structed with its stages of geological change and increasingly complex life is far more impressive than any single, transitory landscape.

Up till now this chapter has talked in terms of natural forces, sometimes in harmony and sometimes in conflict with one another; and up till now, in terms of geological time, they have been the only forces at work. But quite recently a new factor, man, has come on the scene. It is far too early to tell how high he may rank permanently among the agents of erosion, but his record over the short span of recorded history is impressive. Palaeolithic man, who was not a very numerous species anyway, left only the faintest of blemishes—he probably accidentally started a few forest fires—on the face of the earth. Early Neolithic farmers and herdsmen, about 10,000 years ago, took to burning patches of the forest cover in the Middle East, cultivating the clearings until the soil was exhausted, then moving on to burn more trees. But the first settlers in the Negev of southern Israel learned to check erosion in their hills by building a series of terraced dams along the slopes, each dam watering a tiny plot of farmland. After their land was conquered it turned into desert, never to be reclaimed until the present day. Ever since, the spread of civilization—in China, around the Mediterranean, northwards through Europe and across to the New World—has brought denudation of the forest cover, overgrazing by livestock, and consequent gullying and destruction of land by the unchecked run-off of rain-water and the lowering of the water table. The great central European forest, through which Caesar's legionaries could walk for two months without coming to the end of the trees, almost disappeared in the ensuing 19 centuries.

In recent decades there has been some reversal of man-made erosion in the United States. In 1960, new forest growth exceeded forest cutting for the first time since the 17th century. In Italy and the Netherlands, hundreds of miles of new, dry sea-coast land has been reclaimed from the oceans since World War II. But at the same time, the expanding technology of an expanding world population has accelerated man's consumption of all mineral resources. Short of a catastrophe that would decimate the population, nothing is likely to stop this. New energy sources can delay the exhaustion of fossil fuels, but the world appetite for the earth's other raw materials can only increase.

Yet some scientists find hope in the rocks themselves. In every 100 tons of igneous rock, for example, there are eight tons of aluminium, five tons of iron, half a ton of titanium, about a tenth of a ton of manganese, lesser amounts of chromium, nickel, vanadium, copper, tungsten and lead. And in a ton of granite there are a dozen grammes of thorium and a third of that amount of uranium. If the power could be applied to extract all this, then industrial society might keep going indefinitely.

Harrison Brown, geochemist at the California Institute of Technology, has suggested that world population may eventually reach an equilibrium of about 30 thousand million people, who would "consume rock at a rate of about 1,350,000,000,000 tons per year. If we were to assume that all the land areas of the world were available for such processing, then, on the average, man would 'eat' his way downwards at a rate of 3.3 millimetres per year, or over 3 metres per millennium. This figure gives us some idea of the denudation rates which might be approached in the centuries ahead. And it gives us an idea of the powers for denudation which lie in mankind's hands."

TOPPED BY HARD ROCK, THESE JAGGED STONE SPIRES RESIST THE RAINS THAT CARVE THE CLIFFS OF ARIZONA'S MONUMENT VALLEY

The Sculptured Earth

In the relentless rhythm of change, the earth sporadically raises new mountain masses and high plateaux on the continents, while the unceasing motions of water and air wash the dry land into the sea. In the course of their automatic task of diminishing the continents, these forces of erosion often carve a landscape into shapes that men sometimes find beautiful—and always find strange.

BEADED COLUMNS guard the cliffs of Bryce Canyon in southern Utah. They are formed by rain-water running down tiny vertical cracks in the rock, wearing them deeper with each shower. Layers of harder rock wear more slowly, forming bulges in the columns. The pink colour comes from traces of iron oxide (rust) exposed in some of the rocks.

A Plateau's Eventful Past

From the high, arid plateau that covers 130,000 square miles where Arizona, New Mexico, Colorado and Utah meet, the River Colorado each day carries away some 450,000 tons of earth, rock and sand, leaving spectacular formations which include the Grand Canyon (*next page*) and the scenes shown here. In the exposed rocks, geologists have traced a long sequence of dramatic changes. During the first 600 million years a warm, shallow sea covered the area, retreated and returned again and again until it had left layer upon compressed layer of sand and mud in a bed of rock 12,000 feet thick. Then, about 10 million years ago, some huge, unknown force raised the entire region thousands of feet above sea-level, and rains and rivers soon began to chisel the weird landscapes visible today.

TILTED LAYERS of rock in Checkerboard Mesa in Zion National Park, Utah, are the compressed sand-dunes of a prehistoric desert, piled up by the wind and later covered with water.

ERODED STEPS, cut into the Colorado Plateau like part of a giant stairway, progressively expose older layers of sediments, from the youngest rocks, at Bryce Canyon (*upper left*), to the oldest, near the bottom of the Grand Canyon. The tilted fragment of limestone and shale (*lower right*) is the remnant of an earlier cycle of uplifting and erosion.

115

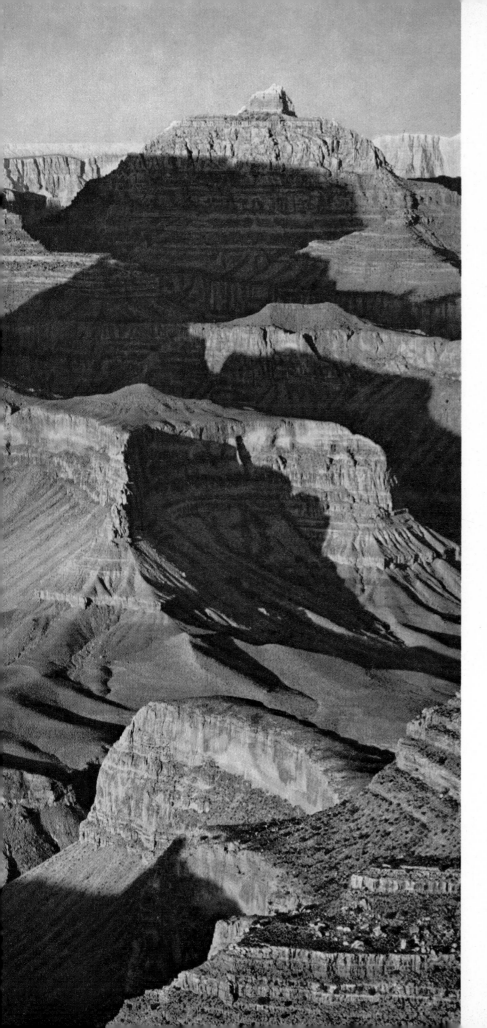

A MILE-DEEP CHASM of glowing colours and shifting shadows, the Grand Canyon is the Colorado Plateau's classic example of erosion. The swift River Colorado gouged the canyon down to its present depth in about 10 million years, and the stream is now wearing away the tough Pre-Cambrian rock at the canyon's bottom at a rate of one foot each 2,150 years.

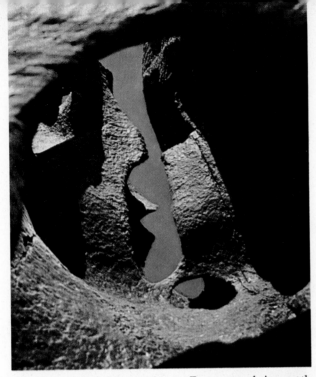

WATER-CUT "CAVES" near Aswan, Egypt, owe their smooth contours to the churning violence of the Nile, which pours through these deep potholes during the annual floods.

The Caprices of Erosion

Unhurried but irresistible, the shifting currents of air and water gradually wear away the surface of the land, producing the familiar forms of hills and valleys, and eventually leaving a landscape flat. But some materials in their path resist this erosion more stubbornly than do others, and where hard rock is interspersed with weaker rock, some grotesque land-forms are carved out, like capricious designs executed in a sculptor's dream.

RAIN AND WIND HAVE SCOOPED OUT A LAYER OF SOFT CLAY FROM

STUMPY COLUMNS, huddled together in the Devil's Garden in Utah, were formed when erosion opened up a maze of deep, vertical cracks in a once-solid layer of rock.

SAND-SMOOTHED ARCH in south-eastern Utah was shaped by abrasive desert winds widening a tunnel which a stream of rain-water had bored through a massive block of stone.

BENEATH THE WEATHERED EDGES OF A BED OF SANDSTONE TO FORM A DEEP, SHADOWED ARCADE AT TOADSTOOL PARK IN NEBRASKA

WIND-CARVED FIGURES of hard sandstone stand on slender pedestals of less resistant rock in Goblin Valley, Utah, their elongated shapes aligned with the prevailing winds.

THICK BOULDERS SHELTER the weak stems of rock beneath them from the rain, which has eroded away about a foot from the rest of this slope on a ridge near Moab, Utah.

The Labours of Moving Water

Among the forces that leave their mark on the continents, streams and rivers do more to change the shape of the land than all the others combined. Steep, turbulent streams batter and scrape the exposed rocks of newly lifted mountain areas with loose bits of stone, quickly digging out steep-walled valleys. A young, vigorous river such as the Colorado can break apart a six-foot boulder and reduce it to mud in four years.

As the jagged contours of the highlands are worn away, rivers enter a less urgent maturity. Their once-steep valleys become broad and flat, and the rivers flow at leisure along winding paths. But even an ageing river can be a formidable agent of erosion: during the spring floods, the Mississippi sweeps daily some 10 million tons of earth from North America down to the Gulf of Mexico.

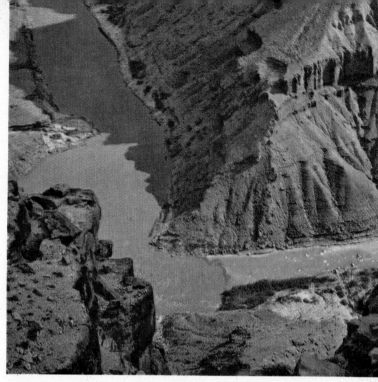

A YOUNG RIVER, the swift, turbulent Colorado (*left*), joins its sediment-laden waters with the clear blue flow of the slower-moving Little Colorado (*right*) in the Grand Canyon.

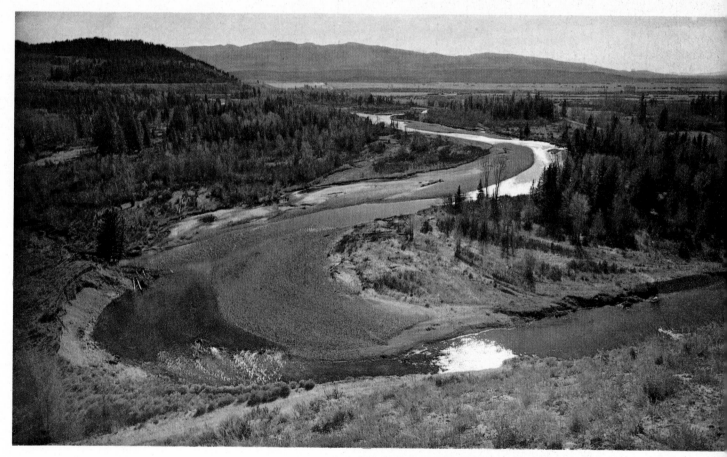

A MISTY PLUME of water, Bridalveil Falls drop 620 feet into Yosemite Valley. After being notched by the stream, the cliff was gouged into its present U shape by a long-melted glacier.

A SEDATE RIVER, the Yellowstone, winds quietly through Yellowstone Park. Its loops steadily widen as the currents cut into the outer banks and pile sand along the inner edges.

CALCITE FORMATIONS IN ELS HAMS CAVE, ONE OF THE MANACOR CAVERNS ON THE MEDITERRANEAN ISLAND OF MAJORCA, GLISTE

The Weird Underground World
of Lost Rivers and Stone Icicles

All rocks contain some minerals which dissolve in water, a fact which hastens erosion and is responsible for the salty flavour of the oceans, where these dissolved minerals have been collecting since the continents first formed. The most soluble of all rocks is limestone, composed of easily dissolved

IN A FLOOD OF COLOURED LIGHTS. STALACTITES GROW DOWNWARDS FROM THE CEILING; STALAGMITES GROW UPWARDS FROM THE FLOOR

minerals from the shells of sea animals. A stream encountering a bed of limestone may eat out in the rock a channel which meanders for miles underground, leaving a string of interconnected caves along its course. The water which seeps into these caves and drips from the limestone ceilings is often saturated with dissolved minerals; as it evaporates, minerals are deposited in icicle-like formations. Water dripping from a stalactite on the roof of the cave will slowly build a stalagmite on the floor below. In time, the two may join to form a single column.

TO RETARD EROSION ON BARE SOIL, STRIPS OF PLANTED LAND ARE LEFT IN THIS RICH GREAT PLAINS WHEAT FIELD IN MONTANA

Erosion's Fertile Debris

In obedience to the law of gravity, erosion carries the land bit by bit down into the sea. If the forces of mountain-building ever stopped operating, all of North America would be worn down to gentle plains only a few feet above sea-level within 20 million years. For mankind, erosion is a mixed blessing. Much of the fine rock debris carried down from the highlands is dropped in lower areas as a blanket of life-giving soil. Depending upon the nature of the original sediments, the rainfall, the mineral content and the organic matter that builds up, these earth deposits may range from barren dusts to the rich black chernozem soils which can support crops in almost limitless abundance. Both the American wheat belt and the Russian Ukraine are overlaid with chernozem. Unhappily, erosion also destroys what it builds. The soils of the plains and valleys are slowly carried seaward, to pile up in deltas or be sluiced away by the flowing tides (*opposite*).

TENTACLES OF THE SEA curl inland, eroding the Dutch coast along the Waddenzee. In this view, from 14,000 feet, a very low tide has revealed pale plains of mud and sand, giving the tidelands the look of a river delta. The darker veins are channels cut deep by the land-stealing sea; when the tide is high they serve fishermen as navigation lanes.

STACKS OF ROCK AT DUNCANSBY HEAD ON THE SCOTTISH COAST ARE REMNANTS OF A PREVIOUS LINE OF CLIFFS. THEY WERE ISOLATED

WHEN THE ROCK BEHIND THEM WAS ERODED BY STORMY SEAS

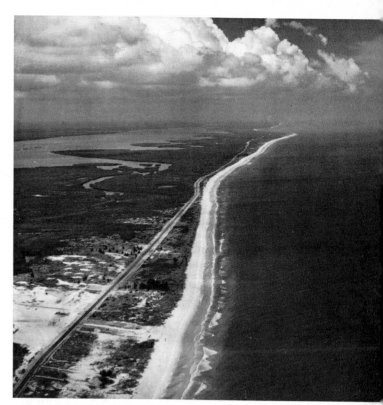

A NEW SEASHORE on Florida's east coast is built of sand washed up by the sea. The old beach and shore-line are visible in the distance beyond the newly enclosed lagoon.

The Sea's Irresistible Power

The ocean cannot match the total erosive power of all the earth's swift streams, but at some vulnerable points its waves shatter the shore like a battering-ram. In its rage the sea can hit a coast with a force of three tons to the square foot, in time reducing rock bastions to stark headlands and sheer cliffs. Often as the sea breaks down the land, it leaves behind such dramatic monuments as the castle-like stacks in the picture on the left. These formations occur when waves attack two sides of a headland and hammer their way through. The first results are sea arches. Then the arches break and their ends, the stacks, stand isolated from the shore.

But the sea can build as well as destroy. Where the shore slopes gently and the bottom is shallow, waves pick up sand and carry it landwards, forming beaches and sand-bars. Once a sand-bar has formed, it may grow to enclose a lagoon (*above*). As waves and wind throw more sand over the bar, dunes build up and fill the lagoon. Thus the land encroaches on the sea.

The Ice-Carved Lands

Erosion by moving ice, in the world of today, is limited to a few glaciers, most of them on high mountains. But during the ice ages, which began about a million years ago, huge sheets of mile-thick ice ground heavily across parts of North America and Europe, leaving the marks of their passing prominently engraved on the land. As the ice advanced over Canada, it bulldozed the soil ahead of it; as a result, much of central Canada is barren, rocky ground while the rich cornfields of the Mid-west thrive in a double thickness of fertile soil. The topsoil of New England was scraped away and deposited off the coast of Connecticut to build up Long Island. As the ice retreated, some of its melted waters collected in the ice-dug hollows where the Great Lakes stand.

A NEWBORN ICEBERG falls from the tip of a Devon Island glacier in the Canadian Arctic. The glacier flows down a steep, gouged valley towering 1,300 feet above the ice.

A PARALLEL PATTERN of rock grooves and ridges, some a mile long and 200 feet high (*opposite*), is the work of an ice sheet that scraped across Victoria Island in northern Canada.

SPLIT IN TWO, this roll-like rock found in Illinois yields its secret— the perfect fossil impressions of a seed-fern frond. The tree-like species lived in the late Carboniferous period, 300 million years ago.

6

The Record of the Rocks

How old is the earth? In recent years the most practical way in which scientists could come to grips with this question has seemed to be in measuring the age of the rocks which form the earth's crust. And this study of ancient strata has certainly provided an enormous number of clues as to our planet's age, the evolution of its life, and the climatic conditions which have existed on its surface during many varied periods in the immensely distant past. However, there is a limit to how far back one can go in this manner, for there was an earlier period during which the earth did not have its present crust—or perhaps any crust. The dating of rocks is useful only back to the time when the rocks themselves came into being.

The measuring stick that is used is radioactive dating, a method which has become available to man in this century, or since he has learned enough about nuclear physics to understand how radioactive materials work. What is useful about a radioactive element is that it has a very precise decay rate, which means that it slowly but steadily, atom by atom, turns into a more stable element. Radioactive carbon, for example, which is created in the atmosphere by cosmic rays, loses exactly half its store of radioactivity in 5,730

0 years—death of animal or plant

5,730 years—1/2 left

11,460 years—1/4 left

17,190 years—1/8 left

22,920 years—1/16 left

60,000 years—about 1/1,000 left

The age of once-living matter can often be determined by measuring its content of radioactive carbon-14. All living things absorb some carbon-14 from the air. When an organism dies, this absorption stops and the carbon-14 it contains begins to decay into nitrogen. Since the rate of this decay is known—carbon-14's half-life is 5,730 years—the age of an organic substance can be established by a count of its radiocarbon. The diagrams above show the rate of carbon-14's decay; opposite are some of the things that have been dated.

years by conversion into nitrogen. A specialist with delicate measuring instruments can compare the amount of radioactive carbon remaining in a fossil with the amount of ordinary carbon, and in that way calculate how old the fossil is. For, in the next 5,730 years, the proportion of radioactive carbon will drop by one half, and in the next 5,730 years, by another half and so on, until ultimately none remains.

Radioactive carbon is a superb tool for the prehistorian, but less useful for the geologist, who is concerned, for the most part, with periods of time vastly longer than its rather short half-life. He must find radioactive materials with half-lives of millions or thousands of millions of years. Luckily they exist. An isotope of potassium decays into argon with a half-life of 1.3 thousand million years; an isotope of thorium decays into lead, and an isotope of rubidium into strontium with half-lives of 14 thousand million and 60 thousand million years respectively.

A particularly useful radioactive tool for geologists is uranium, traces of which are found in many rocks and in widely scattered areas on the earth's surface. All uranium on earth will eventually become lead, with the release of helium in the process. However, this takes place with fantastic slowness. At the end of 2.25 thousand million years, three-quarters of an original chunk of an isotope of uranium will still be uranium, and only one-quarter will have turned to lead.

Today, the oldest known rocks are represented by some granite gneiss found near Dodoma, Tanzania, with an approximate age of 3.6 thousand million years. Older rocks may be discovered in the future; how old, nobody can say for sure. And even the 3.6-thousand-million-year figure leaves open the question of how much older the earth is than its oldest rocks. However, the principle of radioactive dating can be applied to this apparently insoluble problem in a most ingenious way. Recently, radioactive-dating studies have been made of meteorite fragments, giving age estimates as great as 4.5 thousand million years for these bits of solar-system debris. Since it is generally assumed that all the solar system came into being at the same time, most geologists are prepared to accept this as a figure for the earth's age.

WE toss millions and thousands of millions about very glibly. And yet they are such staggeringly large units of time that it is worth pausing to try to emphasize just how long 4.5 thousand million years really is. Hendrik Van Loon did it with this fanciful opening paragraph to his famous book, *The Story of Mankind*:

"High up in the North in the land called Svithjod, there stands a rock. It is a hundred miles high and a hundred miles wide. Once every thousand years a little bird comes to this rock to sharpen its beak.

"When the rock has thus been worn away, then a single day of eternity will have gone by."

A less dramatic but perhaps more useful way of emphasizing the age of the earth is to compare it with the evolution of man. It is generally believed that human beings as we know them today evolved from apelike, non-human ancestors during the last two million years. This slow process of evolution from primitive ancestor to modern man would have to repeat itself more than 2,000 times before the time thus consumed would equal the current estimate of the earth's age.

What is known about the slow process that first brought life into existence on the earth? So far, almost nothing. Biochemists and physicists, arduously calculating backwards to guess at the raw materials which they believe were available in the earth's early atmosphere and in the oceans, have satisfied themselves that the building blocks were there for the formation of protein molecules—assuming that there was a way for protein molecules to have formed. Some recent studies have demonstrated that the lifeless but potentially rich chemical broth in the ancient oceans could have been organized into amino acids through the action of lightning. Amino acids have been turned into protein molecules in the laboratory; from this all else could follow. The major requirement is an abundance of time. It is estimated that the change from simple organic compounds to the earliest one-celled organism may well have taken far longer than the later development from one-celled animal to man. The fossil record shows not only that time was available, but that life did get under way very slowly.

Geologists divide the whole span of earth history into two unequal periods, called aeons. The first, and by far the longer of these, is known as the Cryptozoic aeon, from the Greek for "hidden life". It covers the time from the earliest known rocks up to some 600 million years ago, a span of about 3,000 million years. The second, or Phanerozoic aeon—from the Greek for "visible life"—extends to today.

As might be expected, rocks from the Cryptozoic aeon are by no means the commonest things on the earth's surface. They occur only where the cores of ancient mountain systems have been laid bare by erosion, or where deep gorges have been cut into high plateaux, or, most important, in the form of huge exposed "shields" in a few spots on the earth's surface. In North America the Canadian shield sweeps around Hudson Bay and covers Labrador. In South America the Guiana and Amazonian shields both exhibit vast outcrops. The Ethiopian shield stretches from South Africa to Arabia, the Australian from Perth to Darwin. There is a smaller shield covering most of Scandinavia and, finally, one in Siberia.

These ancient outcrops, rare as they may be in terms of the total volume of the earth's crust, constitute, nevertheless, an enormous amount of material. And yet in all their square miles of bedded limestone and shale, the only fossils that have so far been discovered in recognizable form are a few kinds of algae of the blue-green variety and some colonies of fungus—plus the enigmatic burrows of an unknown worm-like animal. No trace of the ancient worm itself remains.

This seems a pitifully small harvest from a 3,000-million-year segment of earth history. However, it may not be the entire story. Cryptozoan animals were all water dwellers, and probably developed few, if any, hard parts such as shell, cartilage or bone. There may have been many more of them, and a greater variety, than the Cryptozoan rocks show. This possibility is further borne out by the fact that some Cryptozoan rocks are rich in organic carbon, and this could represent the last transient traces of former living things. None the less, the contrast between life on earth even at the end of the Cryptozoic aeon and life in the earliest portions of the Phanerozoic is startling. Whereas we may never devise methods of reading the fossil story of Cryptozoan life, the story that follows it in the Phanerozoic is an elaborate and almost unbelievable chronicle of unfolding evolution. It has taken man a remarkably short time to gather a relatively immense amount of fossil evidence—once he stumbled on the concept that all living things are related and that they trace their descent back to the same origins.

Some of the ancient objects that have been dated by the carbon-14 method appear in the drawing above. A tiny pulse of radioactivity proved the famous Dead Sea Scrolls (1) to be at least 1,900 years old, and some Japanese lotus seeds (2) were found to be 3,000 years old. Sandals (3) in an Oregon cave were carbon-dated at 9,000 years and objects around a skeleton in Illinois (4) at about 10,000. A Wisconsin tree (5) turned out to have died 11,000 years ago, and charcoal (6) found in Iraq kept men warm in 30,000 B.C.

133

The speed at which evolution progresses is a very complex matter and depends on numerous factors, among them geological and climatic change. If such changes are marked, there will be a corresponding tendency towards greater evolutionary change, which is not surprising, since a new set of living conditions may demand differences in animals to ensure survival.

The first step in organizing scientific knowledge is necessarily the classification of material into a useful pattern. In biology, for example, a distinction must first be made between what is a plant and what an animal. The peculiar organisms like slime moulds which are both, or which in some instances spend half their life unmistakably as animals and the other half unmistakably as plants, must be set aside in a special file. But everything else must be organized in such a way that it falls into neat categories, which not only identify the organism but also show its relationship to others like it. The method which the biologist usually uses in classifying animals is to divide them up first into large groups known as "phyla". There are 22 such phyla, which are then subdivided into classes, orders, families, genera and, finally, individual species. Thus, a rose-breasted grosbeak is a particular kind of creature. That is its *species*, since it cannot be subdivided further into different kinds of rose-breasted grosbeaks. However, going the other way, it is a member of a larger group—a *genus*—of grosbeaks, of which there are several kinds in North America, and to all of which it is closely related. Grosbeaks, in turn, belong to a large *family* of finches, and to a still larger *order* of perching birds, which also includes thrushes, crows and orioles, since they have characteristics in common which they do not share with ostriches, for example, or ducks. All these are grouped in a *class* known simply as birds. Birds, finally, belong to a *sub-phylum*, vertebrates, which includes animals with an internal backbone, and finally to the *phylum*, chordates, which includes not only animals with backbones but also those with comparable internal supporting structures.

A startling example of evolution is a small fish called the Blind Cave Characin, which has no eyes. Long ago these fish were trapped in a black subterranean lake in some caves in Mexico. Eyes were of no use in the lightless water, and the fish eventually stopped growing them.

THERE are many kinds of vertebrates which are not birds, and they in turn must be divided into their own subdivisions. At the moment there are found living on the earth seven different classes of vertebrates. There are three distinct classes of fish; a single class of lampreys; a class of amphibians, which includes frogs and salamanders; another of reptiles, which includes snakes, lizards, tortoises and crocodiles; another of birds; and finally one of mammals. In short, there is no backboned animal known which does not fall into one or another of those seven classes.

But the backboned animals are neither the oldest nor the most numerous phylum. Two other very important ones are molluscs and arthropods. The molluscs include clams, oysters and scallops; snails and conches; two other smaller groups of shellfish; and finally squids, octopuses and nautiloids, five orders in all. It may seem that the relationship between a clam and a conch is too close to permit their being placed in separate classes, but when their evolutionary lines are traced back, and the subtle differences which exist between the two are revealed, it will be seen that they are as different from each other as a man is from a fish, or a fish from a bird.

Arthropods constitute by far the largest phylum. This group contains four major classes: lobsters and crabs; centipedes and millepedes; spiders and scorpions; and insects. Again, this may seem like a highly arbitrary division, until it is realized all four have characteristics in common. More important, they share these characteristics with no other living creatures outside their phylum. One characteristic is an external skeleton. It is light and flexible, unlike the shell of a clam and equally unlike the internal bones of a man. "Arthropod" means "jointed legs", and each member of the phylum possesses these. Taken together, there are more than one million different species of arthropods. By contrast there are 132,000 species of molluscs, and about 45,000 chordates. These are the three largest phyla. Without complicating matters by introducing others, it is possible to draw a fairly clear picture of the evolution of life with examples from only these three.

Having classified the animals, we must next classify the conditions under which the animals have evolved. When this is done, the story of evolution may be told. The classification of earth conditions is done by geologists. They know so little about the "hidden" ancient Cryptozoic aeon that they make little attempt to break it down. But the Phanerozoic, extending over the last 600 million years, has been divided and subdivided with increasing precision the closer one gets to the present day.

There are three great subdivisions of the Phanerozoic aeon, known as eras. First comes the Palaeozoic era (ancient life), then the Mesozoic era (in-between life), and finally the Cainozoic era (recent life). Just as the ancient aeon was far longer than the later one, so the three eras show an acceleration in time. The Palaeozoic (subdivided into six periods) drew to a close 230 million years ago, with a total duration of 370 million years. In contrast, the Mesozoic (with three periods) lasted for only 167 million years. The end of the Cainozoic—which began only 63 million years ago—is, of course, not yet in sight. When it will end is impossible to determine, partly because evolution is continuing at an accelerating rate, partly because there is beginning to be a suspicion that man may soon acquire the power (if he has not already got it) of directing not only his own evolution but that of other living things as well, and partly because we have no assurance that our classification of aeons and eras is the best that can be made. Our descendants, human or superhuman as they may be, will certainly be different from ourselves, and they may be so sophisticated or so well informed that they will perceive relationships in past time which are invisible to us, and will be able to make better divisions of eras and phyla than we now make. Be that as it may, the eras are, in turn, divided into periods, as shown in the marginal tables on pages 136 and 137.

The aspect of the earth at the start of the Palaeozoic's first period, the Cambrian, was vastly different from what it is today. The sea occupied a much larger area than it does now, but it was very shallow. The continental land masses were low-lying and relatively small. Their rocks were bare of plant life except for lichens and a handful of other very primitive plants whose spores have since been detected in Cambrian fossil beds. There was no animal life on land at all. The general atmosphere was one of mildness and calm—and apparent agelessness, for the Cambrian period went on and on in this benign manner for 100 million years before sliding imperceptibly into the next period.

Beneath the surface of the sea, however, things were much livelier. The remorseless earlier progression from simple organic compounds to single-celled organisms, and from there to multi-celled forms, had now reached the point where the sea was swarming with a variety of creatures, some of them

Fossils of this sturdy, tongue-leafed ancient fern, the Glossopteris, have been found in such widely separated places as South Africa and South America. This suggests either that its seeds crossed the ocean, or that these land masses of the Southern Hemisphere were once connected.

weighing as much as 10 pounds—millions or thousands of millions of times larger than the single-celled creatures of the earlier days.

The outstanding living form of the Cambrian period was the trilobite, whose name reflects the three lobes into which its body was characteristically divided. If any creature may be called the symbol of a period, then the trilobite was symbolic of those ancient seas. It was the great evolutionary triumph of its time, the most efficient thing the world had ever seen. It was not unlike a cross between a lobster and a sea slug, with an external lobster-like shell and numerous spindly legs which enabled it to creep over the sea-bed ooze. Its segmented body also allowed it to roll up into a tight ball like a wood-louse—presumably for defence. Trilobites developed a wide variety of shapes and sizes, and were so much more advanced than anything else of their day that at their peak they are believed to have represented 60 per cent of all living creatures. And their day was a long one; it lasted more than 300 million years.

The trilobite was an early arthropod, and it shared the Cambrian seas with the pioneers of the mollusc phylum. Of the phylum to which man belongs—the chordates—no member had yet appeared. The ancestor of all the chordates was still scuttling or slithering anonymously around, still in another more primitive form, and it is doubtful if scientists will ever succeed in reconstructing relationships well enough to decide whether their Cambrian progenitor looked more like a worm or a starfish.

AFTER a hundred million years the Cambrian period ended. It was followed by the Ordovician, the change marked by considerable geological disturbance in the Western Hemisphere. The oceans crept in for a time and divided North America into a group of islands. A huge mountain chain reared on the east coast from Newfoundland to Alabama, spawning many volcanoes which scattered their ash as far west as Minnesota. In the seas trilobites continued in enormous throngs, but their pre-eminence was threatened by the emergence of a number of molluscs, among them some spectacular cephalopods. These were cousins of the modern squid and certain of them grew tapering shells that were 15 feet long. The Ordovician period also saw the appearance of the first chordate. In retrospect, this pioneer among animals with backbones was anything but impressive. A fish, it belonged to the primitive jawless variety that is represented in modern times only by the hagfish and the lamprey. Yet this obscure fish *was* a vertebrate, the oldest one that the rocks have so far yielded.

The following period, the Silurian, was much shorter than the two preceding ones, lasting a mere 20 million years. Throughout most of its time it was characterized by the same placidity, the low continents and shallow, warm seas of the Cambrian period. But the eastern United States was slowly transformed by coastal uplift into a landlocked inland sea, which gradually evaporated towards the end of the Silurian period, leaving an immense salt desert. These salt deposits have been extensively mined in New York, Pennsylvania and Michigan. Altogether, the dry salt lake may have extended over 100,000 square miles.

Elsewhere, life in these warm oceans continued to proliferate. The durable trilobite lingered on, but in a strangely modified form. Many types now were covered with bizarre spines, presumably as a protection against the superior mobility and rapacity of the evolving fish. Corals were very common, and were found as far north as Greenland. A gigantic water scorpion appeared, its nine-foot length a record for arthropods. This huge scorpion completely overshadowed an obscure relative, only about two inches long, but which was to be infinitely more important to the overall course of evolution. For this small creature shares with an equally inconspicuous millepede the honour of being the first animal to venture on to dry land. Tantalizingly, the fossil evidence does not reveal whether the respiratory systems of these pioneers were designed for water- or for air-breathing. Hence, we do not know whether they were true land-dwellers or whether they merely nipped in and out of the water.

But the trail blazed by early scorpion and millepede was to become wider and wider. In the next age, the Devonian, 18 spiders are now known to have lived on land, together with a primitive wingless insect whose remains have been found in Devonian rocks in Scotland. However, the most significant advances during Devonian times were made by the vertebrates. Fish had evolved to the point where it was possible to distinguish two major groups: cartilaginous fish such as sharks, and bony fish, ancestral to most modern fish species. Among the latter a particular group went on to develop other novel characteristics which were to prove of immense importance. This group had true jaws. It bore the name of Crossopterygii and boasted two other principal innovations: internal air bladders which could be used as lungs, and stout muscular lobes on the fins. When one considers the conditions which prevailed during the Devonian period—shallow seas which came and went in response to the slow movements of the earth's crust—it seems almost certain that these developments were critical in helping their owners over the hurdle to a land existence. The capacity to gulp air, plus the ability to "walk" on sturdy stumps on exposed tidal flats, is believed by palaeontologists to have been what made the Crossopterygii the ancestors of all the present-day frogs and salamanders.

Of equal importance to the development of vertebrates during the Devonian period was the development of land plants. By this time the appearance of the continents was transformed. The once bare, lichen-dotted, rocky landscapes were now misted with a rich green of giant tree ferns and many kinds of early evergreens. For the first time the countryside looked like a countryside. True, the plants were exotic and spindly, but they were plants, and recognizable ones. There were forests, and quiet pools with fish swimming in them, and insects crawling in the mossy shade.

The great development of plants was continued during the next period, the Carboniferous, which began 345 million years ago and lasted about 65 million years. It was a time of localized crustal activity. Many mountain ranges rose and volcanoes were extremely active. On land, there were vast forest swamps choked with plants and trees. These were buried in water over and over again across huge expanses of the earth's surface. Bedded down in mud, crushed by pressures from the sediments piling up above them, these forgotten forests were compressed into some of the world's great coal deposits, which give the Carboniferous period its name.

Many insects developed during this period, including one that resembled a dragonfly but had a two-and-a-half-foot wingspread. With them came the first traces of a new vertebrate group, the reptiles. These were the first backboned animals to free themselves completely from the water. Amphi-

(Numerals indicate millions of years ago)

PALAEOZOIC
PRE-CAMBRIAN (?-600)
The first life—algae, fungi, soft-bodied marine animals—develops on earth.

CAMBRIAN (600-500)
Trilobites and other primitive arthropods, with a few early molluscs, sponges and worms, dominate the primeval sea.

ORDOVICIAN (500-425)
Marine invertebrates—including clams, starfish, corals, seaweed—share the sea with several kinds of arthropods. Primitive fish, the first vertebrates, appear.

SILURIAN (425-405)
A few primitive animals, including scorpions and millepedes, and some rudimentary plants begin to live on land.

DEVONIAN (405-345)
The vertebrates of the sea grow in variety and size. Several species of fish develop lungs and strong fins and become amphibious. The land for the first time supports large, tree-like plants.

CARBONIFEROUS (345-280)
The first reptiles appear, but giant insects dominate the forests. Fish flourish, including over 200 species of sharks.

PERMIAN (280-230)
Vertebrates—amphibians and reptiles—make rapid progress. Modern insects appear. The trilobite is at last extinct.

MESOZOIC
TRIASSIC (230-181)
Vertebrates, notably reptiles, begin to replace invertebrates as the dominant form of life. The first dinosaurs appear. Lobsters and complex arthropods appear in the sea.

JURASSIC (181-135)
Warm-blooded animals—mammals—make their first appearance, but the reptiles still dominate. Dinosaurs reach their peak and the first birds appear.

CRETACEOUS (135-63)
Dinosaurs, after 100 million years, finally become extinct. Small, primitive mammals increase markedly. Many modern trees develop, among them the birch, elm, oak and maple.

CAINOZOIC
TERTIARY (63-1)
Bony fish abound, and some sharks 60 to 80 feet long appear. Mammals begin to dominate the earth, among them sabre-toothed tigers and early horses.

PLEISTOCENE (1-0)
The age of mammals continues with an important addition—man.

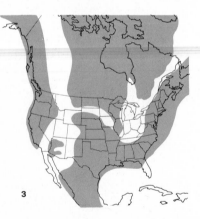

The maps above and on the opposite page show how much of what is now North America was covered by the sea at various times in the distant past. In the Cambrian period (top) the sea covered large areas of the United States although much of Canada was dry land (shown in colour). In the Ordovician period (middle) the sea was even more extensive, although most of the Atlantic coast had risen above the waves. By the late Devonian period (bottom) the land had won considerable gains, but water still covered much of the Middle West and the Rocky Mountain region.

bians must return to water to mate and lay their fragile eggs; their young, just as the tadpoles of frogs still do today, must pass through a free-swimming aquatic stage before they can return to land in mature form. The great innovation supplied by the reptiles was that their eggs had tough cases and could be deposited anywhere without danger of dehydration, and their young could take up a land existence the moment they were hatched. This final liberation from the bondage of the sea ranks as a major event in the history of life.

The last of the Palaeozoic periods, the Permian, was one of the most violent in earth history. Mountain-building increased in intensity, and for the first time in hundreds of millions of years, there was a drastic change in the climate. For the Permian period experienced severe ice-ages which covered parts of Africa, Australia and South America with glaciers. Other parts of the world turned to deserts. Drying seas produced the three largest salt deposits in the world, one in Russia, one in Germany and one stretching from Kansas to New Mexico in the United States. Altogether, this was one of the most inhospitable periods for life ever known, and the strain on many organisms was severe. The denizens of the fetid Carboniferous swamps, both plant and animal, were ill-fitted to withstand the rigours of cold and extreme dryness. Many failed to survive. The great stands of scale trees and seed ferns faded away, replaced by the hardier conifers. Reptiles adapted well, but in the sea the durable trilobite finally reached the end of its career. At last it became extinct.

THUS ended the Palaeozoic period, 370 million years of slow but steadily accelerating evolution. An uncounted number of types had come and gone, but in the process all the major life groups had become well established. The Mesozoic period which followed, and which lasted 167 million years, was notable primarily for the replacement of invertebrates by the reptiles as the dominant type of animal. Once they had firmly anchored themselves on land, these animals experienced a veritable evolution explosion. They were stronger and more agile than the amphibians, which, in the words of Julian Huxley, "pottered with much belly and little leg, like Falstaff in his old age". Throughout the early Mesozoic period reptiles flourished in a great variety of shapes and sizes, gradually getting bigger and bigger as time went on. Some of them returned to the sea in the form of rapacious, dolphin-like animals, but with long, toothed snouts. Others wallowed in the swamps munching enormous quantities of marsh and river plants. By the middle of the era they had evolved into the largest land animals the world has ever known. This was the age of dinosaurs, and although many reptiles were not dinosaurs, the most conspicuous ones were. There was the diplodocus, a "typical" dinosaur with a long neck, a tiny head containing an even tinier brain, a fat body, huge legs and a long tail. End to end, the diplodocus was 85 feet long, larger but not quite so heavy as the similarly shaped but squatter brontosaurus. Tank-like animals called stegosaurs lumbered through the woods, their backs protected by huge, bony plates set on edge, and their tails armed with three-foot spikes. They were slow-moving and even slower-witted creatures, their brains averaging a mere two and a half ounces in weight, housed in a 10-ton body. Another group of dinosaurs were meat eaters. Agile and voracious, they ran along on their hind legs, dangling small forelegs as they went. Some were no larger than chickens. Others, like the allosaurus and the tyrannosaurus, were undoubtedly the most fearsome animals ever known, and preyed on the huge, inoffensive plant eaters. Still others took to the air, gliding over the sea on leathery wings with a spread of 25 feet. These were not birds, nor were they bats. They were flying reptiles with small bodies and thin, hollow bones. Their wings were so enormous in contrast to the size of their other parts that there is a great deal of puzzled speculation as to how they functioned; their legs, for example, were mere fragile appendages, too frail for walking, and are believed to have been used for clinging to cliffs. It is thought that the pteranodon spent all its waking hours gliding over the sea, riding like a kite on the winds rising over the wave crests.

Although the Mesozoic period was dominated by reptiles, the first birds appeared then, as did the first mammals. Both were obscure and unimportant for a long time. But both had adaptations which were clear improvements over what had gone before, and their emergence into a dominance of their own was only a matter of time. Birds and mammals are both warm-blooded, which gives them an immense advantage over insects, amphibians and reptiles. All the latter, if it becomes too hot, suffer heat prostration. A small lizard, living in burning desert sands, must scamper quickly from one patch of shade to another, or it will expire in a few minutes. It is only the bird or mammal, gasping or sweating as it may, which can stay out in the hot sun for long periods of time. Similarly, when the temperature falls, cold-blooded animals become totally inert. Mammals, with fur and a layer of subcutaneous fat to help to retain body heat, and a high rate of metabolism for the continued production of heat, can stand extremes of cold almost indefinitely. They give up a certain elasticity in the process. They require a steady supply of food in order to keep their internal furnaces stoked, the extreme example being the shrew, which must eat heartily every hour or two, or it will starve to death. By contrast, a python needs a good meal only about once a year.

Mammals also suffer if their body temperatures are not kept within a narrow range. An insect may not function well—or it may not function at all—when its internal temperature falls to 1.7° C., but it will not necessarily die. A man will die, however, if his temperature falls below about 18° C. Warm-bloodedness requires constant temperature and a constant supply of energy, but these things are made possible by a far greater mental alertness and physical adaptability. With the need goes the capacity to fill it, and in the last 63 million years, during the Cainozoic era, warm-blooded animals have become dominant.

THIS has been an abbreviated and perhaps somewhat sketchy account of the history of life. Even so, it reveals the vague outlines of some general rules in evolution. Evolution guarantees nothing. It is an accidental, wholly random process. The fact that an amoeba is developed does not guarantee the eventual development of a man. Under the changing conditions on earth, conditions which were themselves shaped by the evolutionary process, man happened to emerge. If the conditions had been slightly different, something else might have emerged instead. And yet there are guide-lines, basic tendencies. There is a trend away from simplicity and towards increasingly complex forms. There is also a tendency for evolving life to flow into a greater number of niches in the environment,

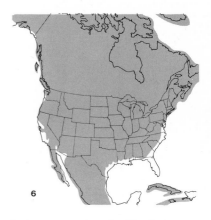

In the great stretches of prehistoric time that succeeded the periods shown in the maps on the opposite page, the seas continued their general retreat from North America. In the Carboniferous period, however, a great ocean almost 2,000 miles wide engulfed western America (above, top), and by the Cretaceous (middle) the sea had once again overwhelmed much of western Canada and all but a small portion of Mexico. Not until the Miocene period (bottom)—about 25 million years ago—did the present continent emerge almost entirely above sea-level.

thus increasing the total amount of life that the planet can support. These two tendencies go together, since greater complexity permits new niches to be explored.

Single cells which accidentally mingle together in groups may, again accidentally, exhibit certain differences between them which make further going-around-together advantageous to the group as a whole. A few may have longer hairs than the average, and the sculling motion of those hairs may enable others in the group to be moved faster than they could move by themselves. Those others, in turn, may ingest food a trifle more efficiently. If such peculiarities were to give a group of cells even the slightest advantage over single cells moving freely in the water, then the chances of survival for the group would be better than for any single cell. Those groups whose useful differences became more pronounced over many generations of further accidental change would have the best chance for survival, and hence the greatest opportunity for further change. In time the differences between individual cells would become so great that they could no longer exist separately. Each would have become specialized for performing a particular function such as sculling, feeding or reproducing. From then on the cells would have to hang together or die, and a true multi-cellular organism would have evolved. In this process the opportunities for further evolution would become greatly enlarged. And evolution itself would show a corresponding tendency to speed up.

All these things have happened. Primitive forms were followed by more complex ones, flowing with increasing abundance and increasing rapidity from the sea on to the land, and into all the cracks in the land. Each period of time had its most efficient and successful type. The trilobites and other arthropods of the Palaeozoic period had their long day of dominance. They were superseded by the reptiles of the Mesozoic period, which were in turn superseded by the far more efficient and adaptable warm-blooded animals of the modern era. Evolution is still going on; the basic tendencies towards increased specialization still exist—and if nothing should occur to interrupt the process, we might be able to assume that in due course another dominant, and better, type would supplant the mammals.

But it must be emphasized again that nothing is certain in evolution. There is no guarantee that this will happen. On the contrary, there begins to be some suspicion that it may not. For the first time in the history of life, there has appeared a creature who is aware of life, and from that time on life can never be the same; for if we become aware of something, we then have the ability to tinker with it.

MAN has evolved to the point where he can reason, remember, read and write, devise scientific instruments and laboratories. Out of this comes the momentous discovery that there is such a thing as evolution. And out of that comes the science of genetics—and with it the key to shaping the further course of evolution. In short, man's future destiny may be guided by him and not by chance. Along with it he will guide the destinies of all other living things. It is unthinkable that he will permit the development of an improved type which might replace him as the dominant organism on earth. Instead, he will choose that type himself and turn himself into it. At least he will have the opportunity to do so. He may not grasp it, but it will be there.

A 50-MILLION-YEAR-OLD RELATIVE OF THE MODERN POMPANO, THIS FOSSIL FISH, MENE RHOMBEUS, ONCE SWAM IN ITALIAN SEAS

The Rich Fossil Legacy

Not all earth's creatures return to anonymous dust. In the ancient rocks that encrust the world are preserved the imprints, and often the bones, of thousands of millions of organisms great and small. For 200 years scholars have studied this fossil record to reconstruct the development of life. Now, to find the basic substance of life, science is penetrating the nucleus of the living cell.

IN A DINOSAUR GRAVEYARD, a skeleton is freed from the rock in which it was preserved. Workmen at the Dinosaur National Monument in Utah use a drill to break the bulk of the rock, and later use more delicate tools. At Dinosaur Monument the remains of many animals are only partly excavated so that visitors can see how fossilization occurred.

FRAIL BLUE BONES are the mineral-impregnated remains of a cat-sized, tree-climbing carnivore called Uintacyon, which roamed the forests of Wyoming some 55 million years ago.

FILMY LEAF IMPRINT, from a platanus tree of the Miocene period, closely resembles the leaf of a modern sycamore. The colours come from minerals that infiltrated the leaf's cells.

The Imprints of Vanished Life

Until about 1750, fossils were widely regarded as the remains of familiar plants and animals drowned in the Biblical flood. With the development of the theories of evolution, scientists looked more closely and recognized the traces of fantastic vanished life-forms, ancestral to modern living things—but quite unlike them in many ways.

It is astonishing that fossils exist at all. Living tissue, even bone, is extremely perishable and, unless quickly buried in some soft material that later becomes rock-hard, will decay and disappear. Often when a scientist excavates a skeleton or a piece of wood, he finds that minerals have seeped into the cells, petrifying them to solid rock. More rarely, only an imprint or a mould of the living thing is found. The internal organs of the insect below decayed long ago, but its mould retains in perfect detail the carbonized outer skeleton.

THE FOSSIL FORM OF A FLY IS PERFECTLY PRESERVED IN AMBER, STICKY PINE RESIN THAT HARDENED 30 MILLION YEARS AGO

Grand Canyon Fossils

The Grand Canyon has a fossil record unsurpassed anywhere on earth. Here the Colorado River has cut into rock strata accumulated over a thousand million years. Near the bottom of the canyon is rock from Pre-Cambrian time, which shows traces of a primitive alga believed to be one of the earliest forms of life on earth. Higher layers have yielded fossils of ever more complex life forms, from the seaweeds and trilobites of the Cambrian period to the large reptiles and trees of more recent ages.

MAYFLY

FERN TREE

STEGOCEPHALIAN

CYCAD

CONIFER

KAIBAB LIMESTONE

UPPER PERMIAN

COCONINO SANDSTONE

SHIP LIZARD

HERMIT SHALE

CORDAITE

SIGILLARIA

NAUTILOID

COCKROACH   SPIDER

DRAGONFLY

SCALE TREE

SHARK

CALAMITE

BRYOZOA

CRINOID

LOWER PERMIAN

BRACHIOPOD

SALAMANDER

SUPAI SANDSTONE AND SHALE

SEED FERN

CLUB MOSS

REDWALL LIMESTONE

CORAL

LUNGFISH

MISSISSIPPIAN

BLASTOID

CEPHALOPOD

CLAM

BRACHIOPOD

DEVONIAN

MUAV LIMESTONE

BRACHIOPODS

EARLY LAND PLANT

CAMBRIAN

STARFISH

TRILOBITE

SCORPION

CRINOID

BRIGHT ANGEL SHALE

TAPEATS SANDSTONE

CORAL

SNAIL

VISHNU SCHIST

PEGMATITE

SEAWEED

PRECAMBRIAN

ALGAE

and the Life of Today

The Grand Canyon today supports a wide variety of animal and plant life. Willow trees thrive in the wet warmth of the river bank, which at places is 6,000 feet below the canyon rim. Blue spruce and Douglas fir grow in the upper, Canadian, zone. With the plant life go the animals that normally live in these various climatic zones. In all their variety, they are a dramatic illustration of the wealth of species that have evolved from the few, primitive forms with which life on earth began.

CLARK'S NUTCRACKER

MOUNTAIN LION

LYNX

BLUE SPRUCE

QUAKING ASPEN

DOUGLAS FIR

CHIPMUNK

MULE DEER

WHITE-TAILED SQUIRREL

CANADIAN ZONE

GOPHER

BROWN BAT

BLUE PENSTEMON

SCARLET BUGLER

WESTERN TANAGER

TRANSITION ZONE

SERVICEBERRY

YELLOW PINE

LOCO WEED

PORCUPINE

RUFUS DEER MOUSE

LIVE OAK

UTAH JUNIPER

BLUE FLAX

CACTUS

BULL SNAKE

SPOTTED SKUNK

ANTELOPE

COLLARED LIZARD

GRAY FOX

CHIPMUNK

GOLDENROD

WILD GERANIUM

UPPER SONORAN ZONE

CACTUS

HORNED TOAD

CACTUS

BAT

MESQUITE

SNOWBERRY

LARKSPUR

KING SNAKE

MOUNTAIN SHEEP

LOWER SONORAN ZONE

JIMSON WEED

WILLOW

GOPHER

A SPOKED HEXAGON at the right, surrounded by a whitish halo, may be a fossil remnant of life from space. It was found in a new study of a meteorite that fell a century ago.

A CELL-LIKE BALL is one of 26 different shapes resembling earth forms that were found in studies of several meteorites. Its colour is from stains used in microscopic examinations.

A PLANT-LIKE SPHERE, shown here in its natural colour (arrow), was discovered in a meteorite that fell in Tanzania in 1936. Under higher magnification it has a band around its middle and is covered with short spines, like many terrestrial algae. Surrounding the sphere is a mass of whitish magnesium sulphate, which is embedded in iron and rock.

Clues to Life's Beginnings

How did the profusion of life on the earth begin? Two recent series of experiments have suggested two possible answers. One group of scientists has examined small particles chipped from meteorites and has found infinitesimal fossils (*opposite*) of what is cautiously described as "organized" material. This implies that life on earth could be a transplant from another planet. Another group of scientists, among them Dr. Stanley Miller (*right*), has conducted experiments which demonstrate that life could have developed here spontaneously when the elements on the primitive earth combined to form the amino acids which are the basis of the proteins of life. After aeons of futile combination and recombination, these amino acids might have formed a complex "Adam molecule", which could grow and reproduce, a spark of life struck off from an infinity of inanimate matter.

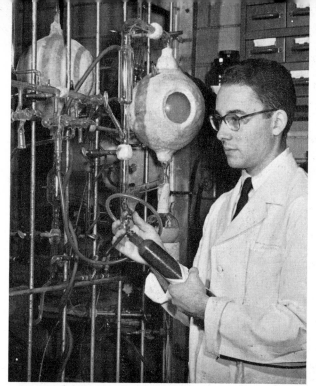

MIXING GASES to simulate the earth's early atmosphere, Dr. Miller shows that this ancient air could have produced organic compounds as possible precursors of life itself.

"ORIGIN OF LIFE" experiment sets out to duplicate conditions under which cells may have originated. First, "primordial" amino acids are heated to form more complex protein- like compounds. When a solution of these is cooled, millions of units like those on the right appear. If the acidity of the solution is then decreased, the units at the centre and left develop.

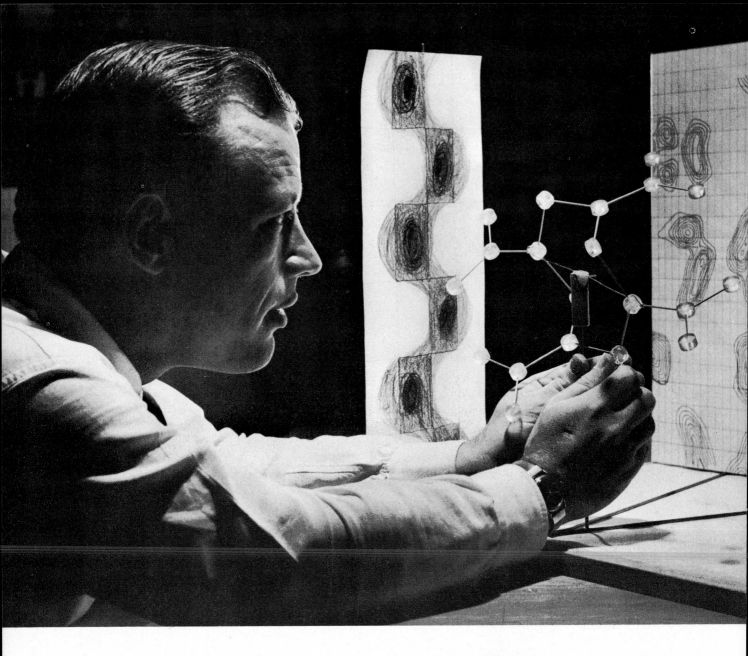

DNA, Protector of Species

Using a vast variety of tools, from electron micro-
scopes to massive computers, scientists in the
last few years have been probing deeper and
deeper into the living cell. At last, within the
chromosomes of the cell's nucleus, they have
identified molecules of deoxyribonucleic acid,
called DNA for short, which is central to all life.

DNA forms an exact pattern determining how
a plant or animal looks and functions. Each species has a different complement of DNA molecules; hence each looks and functions like no
other. Further, the arrangement of DNA molecules is passed from parents to offspring. Thus
there is continuity in the species, dogs always
giving birth to dogs, and humans to humans.

A MOLECULE MODEL is built up from a map of its atomic structure (*above*). Molecules can only be seen indirectly, in the patterns X-rays make on a photographic plate when deflected by atoms.

A MOLECULE PORTRAIT shows an early attempt to map an atomic structure (*opposite*). This is a reconstruction of the atoms of a simple, ringed molecule which is in fact 235 million times as small.

A MOLECULE OF DNA has clusters of atoms which take a spiral shape (*right*). This model of DNA was based on X-ray photographs and other techniques that reveal otherwise invisible atomic structures.

FLU VIRUSES, magnified 35,000 times, appear as irregular balls. Each ball is composed of molecules too small to be photographed by the most powerful electron microscope.

GIANT PLANT VIRUSES cling tightly together like sticky strands of spaghetti. Each long, thin strand forms a virus particle of the type which causes mosaic disease in tobacco.

The Resurrecting Viruses

When life began, it probably flickered uncertainly. An organism might show a spark of life, then revert to the state of inert matter—and, under some stimulus, come to life again. Viruses lead the same flickering existence and are probably much like the earliest life forms in this respect. Viruses can be inert crystals, with no more sign of life than so much table salt, or become living particles (*above*). Composed of a core of nucleic acids in a protein envelope, a virus apparently does not reproduce out of its own matter but makes the cell it attacks turn into a factory producing more virus. An apparently inert virus will assume the properties of life if it encounters fresh cells it can invade. A tiny example of the evolutionary process is shown by the influenza virus, which suddenly developed strains resistant to a vaccine that had been effective against it.

A CLUSTER OF VIRUSES photographed deep within a living cell gathers threateningly outside the nuclear wall. This is the globular fowl-pest virus, enlarged 10,800 times.

CRYSTAL LATTICE A is formed by a virus (*opposite*) which has penetrated the nucleus of a living cell. This honeycomb of crystallized virus has been magnified 94,000 times.

STAGES IN A SLIME-MOULD LIFE-CYCLE SHOW (FROM LEFT) THOUSANDS OF AMOEBAS FLOWING TOGETHER TO FORM A SLUG-LIKE BODY WHICH

Two Microcosmic Miracles

One of the wonders of life is how primitive living cells first banded together to form larger organisms. In what ways did these early organisms survive, reproduce and grow in complexity? To investigate such questions, scientists have studied some of the simple-life forms that still abound on the earth. Two are shown on these pages, a slime mould (*above*) and a hydra (*below*). The slime mould repeatedly goes through a strange metamorphosis in which it takes on characteristics of both the plant and animal kingdoms. First, large numbers of amoeba-like creatures band together to form a new organism which behaves like a worm crawling along on its belly. Then, for some reason, it halts and starts growing like a plant, raising its spore mass on a thin stalk.

A CLUMP OF CELLS FROM A MINCED-UP HYDRA REGENERATES TWO NEW ANIMALS IN THE SEQUENCE BELOW. STUBBY NEW TENTACLES

THEN BECOMES A PLANT WITH A STEM AND A SPORE CASE ON TOP. LIBERATED SPORES BECOME AMOEBAS, AND THE CYCLE IS REPEATED

Abruptly, and just as strangely, the stalk bends and the spore ball bursts, releasing the individual amoebas to start swarming again as the life-cycle of the cell community repeats.

The tiny hydra is remarkable in a different way. Named after the Greek mythical monster that could sprout new heads when one was cut off, it can regenerate itself, perfect and whole, even after it is cut in pieces. Biologists have taken hydras and diced their bodies into microscopic mince-meat. Somehow these scrambled bits of hydra are able to produce complete organisms again. Investigation of this indomitable growth mechanism may provide clues not only to the nature of primitive animals but also to the ability of the cells of higher animals to regenerate damaged tissue.

START TO BUD AT THE CORNERS OF THE CELL MASS, WHICH THEN SLOWLY PULLS APART TO FORM A PAIR OF INDEPENDENT HYDRAS

250,000 TIMES AS LARGE AS LIFE, this six-foot-diameter model reveals the cell's structure. The upper half of the cell membrane has been peeled away to give a clear view of the nucleus (dark region in centre) surrounded by a bustling, organic metropolis in which the stuff of life is manufactured, stored, transported and utilized by a tightly-organized team.

The World within the Complex Cell

All living creatures are made up of one or more microscopic compartments called cells. Amoebae consists of just one. Adult man has about one million million of them. The jumble of lacy plastic ropes and translucent sacs on these pages is a model created by Will Burtin for the Upjohn Company to depict cell structure. Burtin's model represents a basic or generalized cell; the specialized cells vary greatly in appearance, the details of their structure depending on their particular functions.

At the left of the cell model opposite is the nucleus, the headquarters and control centre of the cell. It contains the chromosomes, which are made up of DNA hereditary-governing molecules and give precise instructions for the manufacturing of thousands of different proteins necessary to life. Proteins are synthesized in the ribosomes, tiny units consisting mainly of the secondary hereditary chemical, RNA, and appearing in the model as small red dots. Some proteins are apparently stored in the hemispherical green Golgi apparatus, named after its discoverer, then transported throughout the cell by a network of endoplasmic reticulum, resembling transparent Swiss cheese in the model. To keep these and other vital processes going, energy is generated from the conversion of foodstuffs in the cell's power house, the faintly blue, sausage-shaped mitochondrion.

LIKE A GREEN JELLY-FISH, a little understood Golgi apparatus hovers above the red nucleus. Both float among the seaweed like cytoplasmic fibrils that fill the entire cell.

The Coils of Heredity

Earth's vast variety of life has evolved, over an immense time, from one or a very few simple living specks. Such diversity is possible because an organism is never an exact duplicate of its parents. Thus tiny variations are fed into the stream of life with each generation. Occasionally a very different individual, or mutation, crops up. Most mutations are failures, but rare ones produce a being better adapted to the struggle for existence.

TANGLED CHROMOSOMES, found in the nuclei of living cells, entwine in a beaded pattern. Molecules of DNA, arranged within the beads, are largely responsible for heredity.

A FAMILY OF MICE shows how offspring can vary from their parents. One grey-coloured father (*top*) and five white mothers (*second row*) have produced young (*bottom rows*) of six different colours. Such simple variations are caused by the pairing of parental chromosomes and are not new mutations.

MUTANT AFRICAN VIOLETS offer evidence of the effects of radiation on living things (*opposite*). A violet plant having normal leaves and flowers, like those shown at the centre, was exposed to ordinary X-rays. All the different leaves and flowers round it are mutations resulting from this radiation.

THE FROZEN EARTH about 50 thousand million years from now will be
devoid of life. The moon will draw
closer and the sun die to a flicker.
Man will be extinct—unless he
has migrated to another planet.

7

An Uncertain
Destiny

No sibyl or oracle of ancient times ever performed such prodigies of prediction as today's scientist does when he foretells the swaying of an un-
built skyscraper in a hurricane, the spiralling orbits of an unlaunched astronaut, the qualities of an untried alloy, the vitality of an uncrossed hybrid
or the power of an undetonated weapon. Yet these feats are mere child's
play compared with the attempts of our modern theorists to forecast the global
trends taking place in land, sea and air on our planet. What may happen to
a skyscraper, bomb or rocket is a nearly self-contained chain of cause and
effect. But many natural earth processes are not self-contained, and the number of outside forces which may shape their outcome is legion. Weather over
Los Angeles, for instance, cannot be exactly forecast except as a part of the
total behaviour of the earth's atmosphere. And this behaviour is delicately
modified by faint forces and subtle effects from an incredible variety of sources:
the amount of carbon dioxide released by chimneys, the number of fragments
of disintegrated comets which the earth sweeps up in its path through interplanetary space, the sudden increase in friction between wind and land when
the trees grow leaves in spring.

Such an intricate mechanism as the atmosphere or the oceans or the crust of the earth is known by mathematicians as a "complex system". And the entire earth, embodying as it does gases, liquids and solids, is about as complex as a system can be. The purely gaseous sun, though 10 million times as large as the earth, is far simpler mechanically. Even the universe is simpler, though it undoubtedly contains many thousands of millions of planets like the earth. The reason this can be so is that the complexities of an earth, a sun or even a galaxy have no effect whatsoever on the forces shaping the universe at large. Nothing that happens on earth can influence the future evolution of the sun and nothing that happens on the sun can influence the evolution of the galaxy, the assemblage of 100,000 million-odd stars in which the sun has membership. But the evolution of the universe does affect the galaxy, the evolution of the galaxy does affect the sun and the evolution of the sun does affect the earth. The ultimate fate of the earth can be foretold with absolute certainty because it depends on the mathematically simple system of the universe at large. The short-term future, however, is rich with possibilities which cannot be either denied or definitely predicted.

SCIENTISTS hope and expect that their crystal balls will not always be so cloudy. At Suitland, Maryland, a contingent of government meteorologists, armed with computers, is already calculating the day-to-day weather on the basis of the first crude but comprehensive mathematical models of the entire atmosphere. Moreover, they are constantly improving their equations and their results as they learn to use the over-all global information coming in from orbiting weather satellites. Eventually they hope to gain insight from their studies which will enable them to understand long-term climates as well as short-term weather—to look months, years and perhaps even centuries ahead, and predict world-wide changes in temperature, ocean level and glaciation. If they are successful and can learn to forecast floods and famines well ahead of time, it may take some spice out of life but it will permit nations to forearm themselves against natural disasters and perhaps even to participate in wholesale international weather control programmes.

Since weather is vitally important to trade and commerce, it has been studied more intensively than most earth processes. But man's small, hard-worked cadre of earth scientists is also busy measuring, analysing and correlating the other forces of change which mould the earth's future. Hardly a month goes by in which some scientist somewhere does not uncover neglected factors to refresh the mystery and refine the explanation of some earthly phenomenon which was already thought to be understood. To the oceanic tides of Newton, latter-day physicists have added aerial tides raised in the atmosphere by both moon and sun, and even land tides, two or three inches high, raised in the solid rock of the earth's crust. To the earth's simple axial rotation they have added half a dozen wobbles and precessions. To visible sunlight and starlight they have added a whole spectrum of incoming cosmic energy: radio and infra-red waves, ultra-violet, X-rays and gamma rays, even cannon-balling motes of matter coming from stars which have exploded in the depths of space.

It may well take decades to fit together all the puzzling pieces of evidence into a true portrait of the dynamic earth. No field of science encompasses such a wealth of unexplained facts. All in all, geophysics is a young science with a tremendous number of exciting discoveries lying ahead of it. Until as recently as 1948 the local curvature of the earth in Europe was so little known that the maps of different countries did not join properly. Maps made in Sweden differed from maps made in Denmark by 300 feet. English and French maps were out of mesh by 600 feet.

Limited as modern geophysicists are by quantitative doubts and analytic dilemmas, they can still make a number of confident qualitative predictions about the immediate future of the earth. The continents which have grown out of the ocean from nuclei like the Canadian and north Brazilian shields will continue to grow. The volcanic "ring of fire" which surrounds the Pacific Ocean, pushing up new island arcs and joining them gradually with the mainland, will continue to narrow. California and Mexico will probably continue to expand south-westwards, building on the drowned peaks and plateaux of the East Pacific Rise. Siberia and Alaska, aided by the Aleutian volcanoes, may rejoin permanently and the ancient land bridge of the Eskimos, Indians and mastodons may emerge from the sea once and for all. Britain may be indivisibly added to the Common Market. Patagonia and Tierra del Fuego may fuse with Antarctica to cut off the channel between the Atlantic and Pacific Oceans. On the other hand, the Panamanian Isthmus might sink, creating a new channel. If the islands of the West Indies continue to rise, the Caribbean could become an enclosed sea. The Asiatic land mass may annex Indonesia and possibly even Australia, re-creating the land bridge over which the ancestors of kangaroos and platypuses first migrated Down Under some hundred million years ago.

As the continents grow, and as their granite spreads out over the ocean beds, mountain-building will inevitably slow down. The radio-active heat which mainly powers the earth's orogeny today cannot last for ever. Already the short-lived radioactive elements which were present in the primordial earth have decayed and grown cold. Long-lived thorium, uranium and potassium still supply enough heat to keep the crust restless, but since their combined half-lives work out at about 5,000 million years, they should be building roughly half as many mountains in A.D. 5,000,000,000 as they are today. This should give erosion longer intervals to do its work between successive epochs of mountain-building and should make the average terrestrial landscape a good deal flatter and duller than it is now. The oceans meanwhile will become pent up in ever deepening abysses from which they will spill over as shallow seas on to the broad continental shelves. Of course, if there are descendants of Homo sapiens living then, they may restrict the ocean entirely to its abysses by walling the continental shelves with massive dike-works.

Over the ages, as the inequalities in the earth's structure are gradually ironed out, men and beasts will be plagued periodically by glacial periods. At present the human race is thriving either at the end of the Pleistocene ice-ages or in a brief respite between glaciations. The balance of evidence seems to indicate that modern times are interglacial, but the picture is still somewhat confused. Until recently glaciologists had to rely on such imprecise local gauges as the movements of ice rivers near Swiss hotels or the depths of clay layers at the bottoms of lakes. Now, with the advent of radioactive dating, they have begun to sort out facts from fallacies and assemble a true chronology of ice-age history.

The most extraordinary piece of isotope detective work bearing on the ice-ages has been done by Nobel Prize chemist Harold Urey and a group of his students and associates at the University of Chicago. By measuring the relative abundance of two isotopes of oxygen in fossil sea shells, the Urey group found they could determine the precise temperature of the sea water in which ancient molluscs and protozoa built their hard-hat homes. So delicate is the measurement that developing the instruments to make it took Urey four years. So exact is the perfected technique that it can pin down the season of year in which an ancient oyster was born and the number of years it lived. Using the method on fossil shells of the last 300,000 years, Urey's colleagues found that ocean temperatures throughout the recent ice-ages have varied by about 6° C. in a 40,000-year cycle which exactly corresponds to the ebb and flow of the glaciers on land.

The temperature cycle discovered by the Urey team tends to support an old theory of the ice-ages proposed by the Serbian physicist Milutin Milankovitch in the 1920s. Milankovitch calculated the effect of the earth's many rotational wobbles and orbital deviations on the sequence of its seasons. He found that every 40,000 years circumstances should combine to give the higher latitudes of earth cool summers and mild winters—summers in which glaciers would not melt much, and winters in which snowfall would be heavy over the arctic regions and high mountains where glaciers form.

The Milankovitch theory may explain why temperatures have fluctuated during the ice-ages but it does not explain why the ice-ages first began. During most of geologic time the temperate regions have enjoyed balmy, subtropical climates, enabling palm trees to flourish and leave fossils within a thousand miles of the North Pole. Within the past 30 million years, according to the Urey group, the bottom waters of the ocean began decreasing steadily in temperature, falling from about 20° C. at the end of the era of dinosaurs to a mere 2° C. at the onset of the ice-ages a million years ago.

SEVERAL theories exist to explain the creeping chill which has brought earth's temperate zones to the edge of iciness. The minority view is that the sun has been shedding less heat these last 30 million years. But astronomers generally deny this possibility. Some geophysicists believe that the great cooling must be due to the shifting of the earth and its geography in relation to the closely coupled magnetic and geographic poles. But even here there is little agreement as to what actually moved and how. One school is convinced from their readings of fossil crystalline compass needles that 500 million years ago the North Pole was near Hawaii, 350 million years ago near Japan and since then at various points across the Atlantic until it became ensconced in the ocean now known as the Arctic. At the same time, the South Pole moved out of the Atlantic on to Antarctica, converting it from a subtropical continent into a glacial wasteland.

Lately, these theories of the polar-wandering school have been greatly complicated and perhaps called into doubt by the conclusion that the continents themselves drift around the earth. By 1969, for example, the first fossil excavations in Antarctica seem to have confirmed the long-standing suspicion that regions now exhibiting such wide differences of climate as South America, India and Antarctica were once joined together; as late as the age of dinosaurs they were all combined into one mammoth continent known as Gondwanaland. The name derives from the Gondwana province of India, whose distinctive combination of geological and plant fossils were later found elsewhere. It seems more plausible, many scientists now believe, to account for a great deal of the glaciation in tropical regions and the presence of coal beds in Antarctica by continents wandering across poles or equators than the reverse. And according to this view, many of the world-wide fluctuations of climate may be attributable to the accidental drifting of continents together in such a fashion as to block up some major circulation in the ocean. Since circulation of such currents as the Gulf Stream serves to moderate the world-wide climate, such stoppages could have had profound influences.

Either polar or continental wandering could have brought on ice-ages by reducing the earth's energy intake: by changing dark, heat-absorbing areas of the land into snow-covered, reflective areas. As long as the poles were at sea, their ice packs must have been held in check by the moderating warmth and dispersing currents of the ocean. But when great land areas turned frosty white, the earth must have taken in less of the sun's heat every year, and gradually the whole earth must have grown colder. When the oceans were no longer able to supply enough heat to counteract the trends on land, the glaciers were presumably free to advance and retreat in response to the Milankovitch cycle.

The future of the moon, according to one theory, is shown in these drawings. Above, the moon is still in its accustomed orbit around the earth and looks as it does today.

THE best evidence of the oxygen-isotope shell thermometers indicates that the interglacial climate reached its warmest about 8000 B.C. and has been intermittently cooling down since then. Its fluctuations seem to have coincided with several great historical events. The warm era some 10,000 years ago probably dried up the Sahara and forced the people of North Africa into the oases of the Nile, where they founded civilization. Prolonged cold snaps in pre-classic times and again in the early centuries of the Christian era may have helped to propel barbarian hordes south-westwards out of Central Asia against the walls of Knossos, Troy, Rome and Byzantium. A balmy spell about A.D. 1000 probably enabled the Vikings to discover Iceland, Greenland and America. Since about 1720 the ocean temperature has risen slightly but it could shortly turn down again.

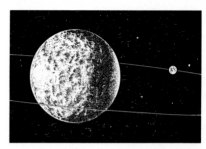

For several thousand million years, the moon will spiral farther into space, increasing its orbit to compensate for the decrease in the speed of the rotation of the earth.

If the glaciers do grind slowly south again over the next few thousand years, man will either have to migrate into the tropics and the no-longer-dry desert zones of the earth or he will have to spend considerable power and ingenuity diverting the streams of ice away from his northern cities. If, on the other hand, the poles or continents shift or the sun burns hotter, the ice-ages will come to an end and the tremendous volume of water locked in the ice-caps of Greenland and Antarctica will be released to raise the level of the oceans by an estimated 200 to 300 feet. Then man will either have to move or expend enormous energy and intellect. Either he will have to abandon his coastlands and great port cities or, if he has gone on improving his technological proficiency, wall the entire seaboard of Europe and America with dikes thousands of miles long.

The moon, spiralling back to earth later in response to the earth's faster rotation, caused by the gravitational pull of the sun, may come close enough to shatter.

It is highly likely that industrial man by his very existence will artificially modify the cycles of the ice-ages or abolish them. Over the last 100 years, factory chimneys have poured 320,000 million tons of carbon dioxide into the atmosphere and almost an equal amount has been released by soil cleared of forest for farming. Some of this gas has been quickly captured by dead leaves, living things and other organic material. The rest has risen into the air, increasing its carbon dioxide content by about 13 per cent. Since car-

In the final stage, thousands of millions of the moon's fragments would circle the earth as tiny satellites, creating a ring similar to the ones now seen around Saturn.

163

The burning-out of the sun will take thousands of years. Above, the sun is at the strength it has held for 5,000 million years and will retain for a similar period.

Helium is forming at the sun's core. Expanding over 5,000 million years, it will transform the sun into a red giant, turning the earth's oceans to clouds of steam.

After about a thousand million years as a red giant, the sun will begin to shrink back to modest size, but it will be in its death throes by then and its brightness will slowly fade.

About 15,000 million years from now, the sun will be a white dwarf, its fires almost out. As it contracts more and more, the earth in time will be a dark, frozen mass.

bon dioxide in the atmosphere prevents the escape of heat from the earth into space, this change in the air's content should have raised earth temperatures by about $\frac{1}{2}°$ C. Actually, during the century of industrialization prior to 1940, the average world temperature did show such an increase. Since 1940, however, there has been a slight but puzzling *decrease* of about 4°, despite outpourings of CO_2 that have more than doubled during that time. Trying to account for this, some meteorologists have pointed a suspicious finger at another product of man's ceaseless activity—smoke and dust. Careful measurements indicate that atmospheric "turbidity"—or murkiness—has noticeably increased over the past century and thus might have begun to offset the heat-trapping effect of the CO_2. The particles themselves not only shade the earth but act as nuclei on which moisture collects, promoting the formation of clouds that shade the earth and further reduce the amount of solar energy reaching it. Such findings merely serve to underline how delicate are the balances that keep the world habitable.

THE Herculean labours which the dynamic earth may exact of the human race during future floods and glaciations are as nothing compared to the challenges which will come from outside the earth. The first and least serious threat will come from the moon. The tides it raises in the land, sea and air are gradually slowing down the earth's spin. At present the rotation period is lengthening at the rate of about 25 thousand-millionths of a second each day. This seems little, but after 5,000 million years it will give the earth roughly a 36-hour day. Man and his crops should be able to adjust themselves to roasting 18-hour days and equally long cold nights but the effect on the atmosphere—especially on the creation of tornadoes and tropical hurricanes—may well be catastrophic. The earth's slowing rotation will be accompanied by a second phenomenon: the energy of spin which the earth loses will be picked up by the moon through gravitational linkage and as a result the moon will move into a larger orbit, spiral outwards from the earth and shine more faintly in the sky. At present the moon is departing from the earth by about one foot every 30 years. But this rate will decrease as it goes farther out because of competitive effects caused by the sun. The alternate heating and cooling of the earth's atmosphere by sunlight works to speed up the rotation of the earth. When the moon's pull on earth becomes weakened because of its increasing distance, the sun's speeding of earth rotation will overcome the moon's slowing of earth rotation. The earth will turn more quickly again and will begin to pull the moon inwards once more. This will probably happen in about 5,000 million years, when the moon is nearly half again as far from the earth as it is today. At that point in the moon's future the sun itself will change, quickening the moon's return towards earth and intervening in earth's evolution so dramatically that for a while further lunar developments will seem inconsequential.

Astronomers know how the sun will evolve because they have studied sun-like stars, older than the sun, and have seen how they behave as they begin to run out of the nuclear fuel which makes them burn. When a star of the sun's mass has converted 15 per cent of its original hydrogen into helium by the H-bomb fusion reaction, the helium ash at its core lights up in a second nuclear reaction which is far hotter. As a result the star begins to pour out energy at an increasingly profligate pace, swelling and turning blood red as it does so.

Between about five and six thousand million years from now the sun will swell from its present size until it fills most of the volume between itself and the innermost planet, Mercury. At the prodigal height of its power, its width will cover a full twelfth of the arc from one earth horizon to another and its outpouring of energy will raise the terrestrial temperature to well over 500° C., a heat so grilling that tin, lead and zinc will long since have melted, the oceans will form an enveloping cloud of steam, and sulphur—the Bible's brimstone—will boil on the earth's surface.

After the lethal climax of its life the sun will gradually shrink again and the waters of the firmament will return to flood the earth a second time. For a few hundred million years the sun will burn blue as it converts the last of its nuclear fuels into metallic elements. During the course of its senescence it will possibly go through unstable stages in which eruptions in its outer layers will lay bare its blazing interior and expose the earth to devastating doses of X- and gamma rays. Finally it will consume the last of its nuclear energy and lapse into permanent quiescence. The waters of the earth will then freeze into a permanent mantle of ice. As the sun cools further, it will continue to shrink under its own weight and will glow feebly for a long, long time. The shrinkage will not affect the orbit of earth because the sun's mass will not decrease: its matter will simply grow more dense. Altogether, in the entire span of life, the sun will have turned only about one thousandth of its matter into energy, and this will represent a loss of mass far too small to loose the bonds of gravity binding the earth in its ceaseless round of the heavens. Ultimately, after a lifetime of some 60 thousand million years, the sun, completely darkened, will course onwards through space only as the black corpse of a star, shrunken to incredible density and taking up no more room than a planet. In its final state of inert self-compression it will actually be smaller than the earth, but its huge mass will still keep the earth locked in orbit around it.

WHILE the sun is dying, the moon will probably be spiralling in towards the earth. As long as the sun remains hot, the inward movement should continue. Conceivably it could bring the moon so close to the earth that the difference in pull of the earth's gravity on its near and far faces would finally shatter it into fragments. The fragments, grinding themselves smaller and smaller by constant collisions with one another, would eventually form into rings like Saturn's, girdling the earth's equator in a washer-shaped disc of debris. But modern theorists have begun to doubt that the sun will remain hot enough long enough for this to happen. They suggest that the sun will go through its final phases too quickly for its heat to bring the moon within shattering distance. Instead, the moon's tidal effects will take over again and the moon will once more pull away from the earth. As it drifts off it will have little light to reflect and the nights will become darker and darker until it is no longer visible at all. As for the days of that bleak, remote epoch, lit only by the wan and watery light of the fast-fading sun, they will be little brighter than modern moonlight nights.

Scientists generally assume that the human race will not live long enough to suffer in the fiery swelling of the sun or the dark doom of the moon. The average life of any one animal species revealed by the geological record in the rocks of earth is only about a million years—a million years compared to five thousand million years before the sun even begins to swell and embark on the last apocalyptic violences of its career. Even though it is logical to conclude that man will fare no better, he might just do so. Some species have survived unchanged on earth for hundreds of millions of years. What is more, the human species is not subject to the same laws of evolution that have operated up to now. Already man so dominates his planet that the natural evolution of most land plants and large animals has been drastically altered. Man's own evolution has also escaped from the natural channels. On the debit side, it no longer encourages fitness through survival since it no longer prevents the reproduction of individuals with weaknesses like congenital diabetes or low intelligence. On the credit side, it has ceased to be a physical evolution at all and has gradually become a cultural and social one.

UNDER the circumstances no scientist, when pressed, will insist that the human race is subject to the same inglorious laws of survival as those which determined the course of pre-human evolution. None the less, most scientists persist in taking a gloomy view of man's ability to survive his own predatory nature. Whether this pessimism is justified remains to be seen, but if the human race does outlive its warlike proclivities and murderous instincts, it may well plan to outlive the sun as well. Colonizing other planets around stars burning more slowly than the sun may possibly provide a temporary escape for a few fortunate astronauts and astronautrixes. For the entire race of human descendants remaining on earth, however, there conceivably would be a more democratic and economical escape.

At its worst, the sun will not scald the earth with heat and cosmic rays so lethal that human intelligence could not devise a shield against them. It may be that when the heat-death approaches on earth some five thousand million years from now, some human form of big-headed, small-limbed intelligent life will already have gone underground, taking with it as much of the earth's air and water as possible, and coating the outside of its single huge planetary survival shelter with pyro-ceramic mirrors which will deflect most of the sun's scorching heat back into space.

Afterwards, as the sun cools, *Homo futurus* may be able to come out of his artificial caves into the open again and finish his preparations for the eternal night and cold ahead. If he has been able to preserve a half of the earth's present water, he will have enough hydrogen fuel for his thermonuclear reactors to be able to power the earth as liberally as it has now been powered by the sun for a period of 10 thousand million years. Since most solar energy today is wasted, he should be able to eke out his reserves still further, perhaps for 10 million million years, giving himself a future on earth 1,000 times as long as the entire history of the earth previously. Nor would that be the end of his resources. The planet Jupiter contains about a thousand times as much hydrogen as the earth, and if he could build power reactors on Jupiter, he could beam energy back to earth so frugally that almost none would be lost. The engineering difficulties would be stupendous and, of course, the entire possibility at this great distance in time and civilization—when man has existed for a mere million years—is entirely speculative. The fact remains, however, that science has found no reason yet why *Homo futurus* should not extend his spiritual evolution almost indefinitely far into the future, if he can once make up his mind to live as a purely intelligent creature instead of a half-intelligent, half-instinctive semi-brute.

A MOB OF CHINESE JAMS A STREET IN SHANGHAI. WITH 800 MILLION NOW, CHINA WILL HAVE A THOUSAND MILLION MOUTHS TO FEED BY 1981

The Crowded Future

Thousands of millions of years before the world ends in some celestial disaster, man must learn to manage it better, lest he manage his own premature extinction. Pressing problems confront the race—not the least that of finding standing room. The past saw a squandering of resources; the present is witnessing a search for new ones. The future will reveal whether they are found in time.

167

CROWDING EVERY BIT OF LAND, THIS PUERTO RICAN SLUM, KNOWN AS "THE MUD PUDDLE", PUSHES OUT INTO THE WATER AT SAN JUAN

The Goad of Overpopulation

Ever since 1798, when Thomas Malthus propounded that the world's population would outstrip the world's food supply, pessimists have been saying that mankind is breeding for disaster. Where there were four of us 10 years ago, there are now five; and the earth's population of 2,500 million in 1950 will swell to over six thousand million by 2000. But the Malthusian arguments are based on the premise that the earth has a fixed capacity to support mankind. That capacity, however, has proved most flexible.

Today a densely populated but scientifically cultivated Holland provides every Dutchman with a good and varied diet, produced on only two-thirds of an acre. If Dutch efficiency could be applied to agricultural methods in needy areas, there would be enough food for 30 thousand million people, nearly 10 times the world's present number. In Japan, where population has increased about 134 per cent since 1885, food production has gone up by more than 300 per cent. Taking Japanese standards of diet and agriculture, food could be provided for 90 thousand million people. Thus, while it holds the seeds of disaster, population growth can also be a goad—perhaps the only one that can force man from old, earth-wasteful ways.

TERRACED FIELDS in overcrowded Japan (*right*) are divided among the 11 families shown here, each tilling three acres. Japan has only one-tenth of an arable acre per person.

UNLESS POPULATION GROWTH CAN BE CONTROLLED, NEW HOUSING PROJECTS ARE SHORT-RANGE SOLUTIONS TO SUCH URBAN CONGESTION

EVISCERATED LOOK of the world's largest open-pit iron mine in Minnesota testifies to the depletion of mineral resources. Once considered an inexhaustible supply of high- grade ore, the Hull-Rust-Mahoning mine now yields low- quality ore refined from taconite, the hardest rock quarried in the world. New methods make this economically feasible.

NEW TECHNIQUE FOR MINING LOW-GRADE IRON ORE BY USING A FLAME OF NEARLY 2,500° C. TO PIERCE HARD ROCK

The Irreplaceable Ores

The world's mineral wealth is running out. Even the United States, one of the richest natural storehouses of minerals on earth, is facing shortages. Between 1900 and 1950, when its population doubled, its consumption of minerals went up by six times, and by 1975 that rate will probably double. Already, world reserves of such essentials as copper, lead and zinc are considered inadequate. As the search for new sources goes on, it is clear that methods of exploration and ore extraction must be vastly improved to keep costs from soaring. But as high-quality ore in Minnesota neared exhaustion a few years ago, production of iron from taconite, a hard rock containing ore (*above*), was achieved. What happens when all the iron in the world is used up? Substitutes may be found, or perhaps men will be able to fish nickel-iron asteroids from space to supply earth with ore.

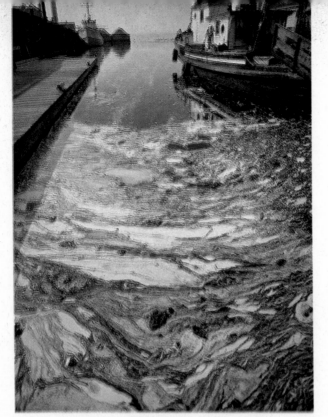

SCUMMY WATERS of a harbour in Washington State are polluted with wastes. Pollution is a growing menace everywhere, even though millions are being spent to combat it.

...And Not a Drop to Drink?

Water, man's most precious resource, is the one he has most recklessly squandered. In the U.S.A. the consumption of water per person is a staggering 50 gallons a day, a figure that will probably rise to 70 in the next 30 years. Already, the city of Los Angeles has drunk a 25-by-20-mile lake dry. Industrial wastes increasingly contaminate rivers and harbours (*left*), killing fish. Sewage does its dirty work too: in 1961 it added twice as much pollution to U.S. waterways as was considered a permissible limit in 1951.

Conservation and re-usage of water are partial answers to the problem. But the world's real hope lies in making salt water fresh. Efforts range from small solar stills to the world's largest distillation plant, in Kuwait, which produces about four million gallons a day. Costs in many areas are prohibitive, but when they are reduced —perhaps by use of some new cheap fuel—the double threat of drought and famine may vanish.

A HOARDED RESERVE of water in India, for use during the drought season, is enlarged by deepening its bed (*above*). The scores of workers are volunteers from near-by villages.

A VAST SUPPLY of water for the American South-West is held by the Glen Canyon Dam (*opposite*) on the river Colorado. Its 700-foot-high wall backs up a 185-mile lake.

172

Where the Water Is—and Is Not

in the Thirsty United States

A water map of the continental United States shows areas where water is plentiful and where it is scarce. Twenty basins are indicated, each based on river flow and topography. The basins are numbered in the order of water scarcity: thus Basin 1, the upper Rio Grande and Pecos region, has the least water; and Basin 20, the South-East, the most. The regions coloured white, yellow, orange and brown are water-

CANADA

MAINE

⑮ NEW ENGLAND BASIN

MINN.

⑭

UPPER MISSISSIPPI BASIN

Minneapolis

Wis.

⑰

GREAT LAKES BASIN

MICH.

N.H.

VT.

Boston

MASS.

CONN. R.I.

N.Y.

Hudson R.

St. Lawrence R.

IOWA

Mississippi R.

Chicago

IND.

⑱

OHIO BASIN

OHIO

Illinois R.

ILL.

Wabash R.

Ohio R.

Allegheny R.

PA.

Susquehanna R.

Delaware R.

New York

N.J.

MD.

Washington

DEL.

⑩

DELAWARE AND HUDSON BASIN

Missouri R.

⑧

LOWER MISSOURI BASIN

St. Louis

MO.

W. VA.

⑬

CHESAPEAKE BASIN

VA.

Cumberland R.

KY.

⑫

TENNESSEE BASIN

N.C.

D RED BASIN

White R.

⑪

LOWER MISSISSIPPI BASIN

TENN.

Tennessee R.

S.C.

⑯

LOWER ARKANSAS RED, AND WHITE BASIN

KLA.

Red. R.

ARK.

Mississippi R.

Tombigbee R.

ALA.

Alabama R.

⑳

SOUTH-EAST BASIN

GA.

Atlantic Ocean

MISS.

LA.

Mobile R.

Apalachicola R.

ULF BASIN

TEXAS

Houston

New Orleans

FLA.

Miami

poor areas; those coloured blue are water-rich—the deeper the blue, the more plentiful the water. The average yearly rainfall in the United States as a whole is a substantial 30 inches (3,500,000,000,000 gallons a day), but rainfall varies from 140 inches in the Pacific North-West's Olympic rain forest to two inches in Death Valley. Nearly a quarter of the average rainfall is carried off by the country's rivers. On this map, the width of a river indicates its comparative rate of flow. The Mississippi carries 300 thousand million gallons a day into the Gulf of Mexico; the Colorado carries seven thousand million gallons a day to the Gulf of California. The East, with 75 per cent of the nation's water supply, uses only 2 per cent of that share. The thirsty West uses 65 per cent of its 25 per cent share; by 1980 Westerners may face an acute water famine.

175

POWER SOURCE OF THE FUTURE, a nuclear reactor submerged in a protective pool makes the water glow blue with its radiation. A chief advantage of nuclear power lies in the concentrated nature of its enriched uranium fuel, one pound of which can produce approximately the energy released by burning the coal carried by a freight train.

FOCUSED RAYS OF THE SUN MELT A HOLE IN STEEL

A Limitless Supply of Energy

Only 20 years ago men worried about world energy sources. There was only so much coal and petroleum in the earth, and while not all these fuels had been located, they seemed bound to give out in time. Hydroelectric power could hardly turn the gears of civilization or run its motor-cars. Today, the energy supply is unbounded. The breakthrough came on the 20th December, 1950, in a laboratory in the Idaho desert, when scientists generated electricity from atomic energy for the first time. The significance was that radioactive fuels contain much more energy than any others (*opposite*); and uranium reserves alone are 10 times those of coal, oil and natural gas in terms of extractable energy.

Since that historic advance, other new sources of energy have been tapped. The sun has been used to heat houses, melt steel (*above*) and power satellites. An atomic bomb in New Mexico produced an underground reservoir of hot (760° C.) liquid salt, into which water was injected to form steam which could run a turbine. Even bacteria have gone to work too. Germs feeding on sugar in sea water have powered a radio transmitter, and it is possible that bacteria-generated electricity could convert salt water into fresh water, and perhaps nitrogen and phosphorus into fertilizers.

THE GIANT MIRROR of a French solar furnace focuses the sun's rays into an oven, where temperatures go up to almost 3,000° C., roughly half as hot as the sun's surface.

WEATHER CONTROL is attempted in this early experiment. Dry ice scattered from a plane cuts a race-course pattern in the moisture-laden clouds, forcing them to disgorge rain.

MAKING RAIN, Dr. Bernard Vonnegut demonstrates his early method of vaporizing silver iodide with a charcoal burner (*below*). The vapour condenses water from the clouds.

First Steps to Weather Control

The new science of weather control was born nearly two decades ago when meteorologists seeded clouds with dry ice and silver iodide to induce rain (*opposite*) and dissipate clouds and fog. By 1969 Project Stormfury achieved more startling effects, seeming to weaken Hurricane Debbie with two seedings of silver iodide. But reliable weather control remains impossible until the complexities of atmospheric processes are unravelled, requiring such large-scale, costly research as that of BOMEX (Barbados Oceanographic and Meteorological Experiment).

An intensive three-month study carried out east of the Caribbean island of Barbados, BOMEX mobilized not only a special barge that stands on end (*right*) but also 1,500 men, 10 ships, 24 aeroplanes, thousands of balloons and buoys, 7 space satellites, 7 federal agencies, universities and independent research laboratories in the United States, Canada and Barbados. Millions of separate measurements of cloud patterns, temperature, humidity, wind velocity, ocean currents and salinity were fed into computers.

BOMEX's aim was an understanding of the source of the earth's weather, the equatorial belt of warm oceans where the sun's heat turns sea water into water vapour and lifts it into the atmosphere to be transported north and south by fast-moving air currents. This results in an interchange of energy that causes all the baffling manifestations of the weather. The evaluation of BOMEX's data was expected to take years; the eventual goal is precise weather forecasting for longer periods—and ultimately weather control.

RESEARCH BARGE FLIP is upended by flooding her ballast tanks. When righted, the odd-shaped craft rises 55 feet vertically from the sea while a 300-foot length of submerged ballast keeps FLIP from bobbing. During the BOMEX project precise measurements of the movement of water vapour from the ocean were made from the rock-steady FLIP.

EAVESDROPPING ON SPACE with an 85-foot-wide dish antenna, a radio telescope in West Virginia, shown in a star-streaked time exposure, listens for radio signals from planets or stars during 1960's Project Ozma. Though the results were negative, the experiment pointed to the day when improved equipment will permit communication by radio with

A "COCKPIT" RUNS THE LARGEST RADIO TELESCOPE AT JODRELL BANK

Is Anyone Talking Out There?

In reaching for the stars, man finds himself humbled by them. The astronomers estimate that the Milky Way, only one among thousands of millions of galaxies, has at least 100,000 habitable planets and concede that the intelligence of beings on them could equal or exceed our own. Until a few years ago, there was no hope of communicating with the stars. Now the huge mesh ears of radio telescopes permit man to hear the electric impulses that bombard the earth from space. Out of this stellar static may one day come a message, perhaps only a simple mathematical equation like the ones below, to end man's loneliness in the universe.

other worlds. A new device, called a "laser" and employing a synthetic ruby to produce a pencil-thin beam of light, opens up the possibility of sending messages with pulses of light.

INTERSTELLAR TALK could start off with mathematics, as shown above. Numbers would be counted out with electronic blips; other signals would stand for arithmetical symbols.

Count-Down to the Future

Man's achievements in space are already beginning to catch up with science fiction. In the last decade he has sent instruments, animals and humans whizzing around the earth, fired robot space craft to Mars and Venus and landed astronauts on the moon. Manned flights to Mars and Venus are being planned. Interplanetary travel may be commonplace by the turn of the century and trips outside the solar system are conceivable in the next 100 years. Perhaps some day man will be able to outlive his ageing earth by migrating to another earth-like planet somewhere in space.

IN DAZZLING SUNLIGHT ON THE MOON, astronaut Alan Bean carries instruments from the Apollo 12 Lunar Module to measure quakes, magnetism and other lunar conditions.

A FIERY TRAIL is traced in the Florida sky in this rocket launch of a U.S. moon probe (*opposite*). Plans exist for using the moon as a giant base for trips to deeper space.

Bibliography

Geology and Geography

Brown, Lloyd A., *The Story of Maps*. Cresset Press, 1951.

Dunbar, Carl O., *Historical Geology* (2nd ed.). John Wiley, 1960.

Eardley, A. J., *Structural Geology of North America*. Harper & Brothers: Hamish Hamilton, 1951.

Emmons, William H., Ira S. Allison, Clinton R. Stauffer and George A. Thiel, *Geology: Principles and Processes* (5th ed.). McGraw-Hill, 1960.

Longwell, Chester R., and Richard F. Flint, *Introduction to Physical Geology*. John Wiley, 1962.

Namowitz, Samuel N., and Donald B. Stone, *Earth Science* (2nd ed.). D. Van Nostrand, 1960.

Raisz, Erwin, *General Cartography* (2nd ed.). McGraw-Hill, 1948.

Shimer, John A., *This Sculptured Earth*. Columbia University Press: Oxford University Press, 1959.

Strahler, Arthur N., *Physical Geography* (2nd ed.). John Wiley, 1960.

Trewartha, Glenn T., Arthur H. Robinson and Edwin H. Hammond, *Fundamentals of Physical Geography*. McGraw-Hill, 1962.

Von Engeln, O. D., *Geomorphology*. Macmillan, New York, 1942.

Wyckoff, Jerome, *The Story of Geology*. Books for Pleasure, 1962.

Zeuner, Frederick E., *Dating the Past: An Introduction to Geochronology* (4th ed.). Methuen, 1958.

Geophysics

Bullen, K. E., *Seismology*. Methuen, 1954.

Chapman, Sydney, *The Earth's Magnetism* (2nd ed.). Methuen, 1951.

Gutenberg, Beno, *Physics of the Earth's Interior*. Academic Press, 1959

Howell, Benjamin F. Jr., *Introduction to Geophysics*. McGraw-Hill, 1959

Jacobs, J. A., R. D. Russell and J. Tuzo Wilson, *Physics and Geology*. McGraw-Hill, 1959.

Jeffreys, Harold, *The Earth* (4th ed.). Cambridge University Press, 1959.

Kuiper, Gerard P., ed., *The Earth as a Planet* (*The Solar System*, Vol. II). University of Chicago Press, 1954.

Landsberg, H. E., and others, eds., *Advances in Geophysics* (9 vols. to date). Academic Press, 1952-62.

Munk, Walter H., and G. H. F. Macdonald, *The Rotation of the Earth*. Cambridge University Press, 1960.

Parasnis, D. S., *Magnetism*. Harper & Brothers, New York, 1961.

Richter, C. F., *Elementary Seismology*. W. H. Freeman, San Francisco, 1958.

Upper Atmosphere

Beiser, Arthur, and Germaine Beiser, *The Story of Cosmic Rays*. E. P. Dutton, New York, 1962.

Chamberlain, J. W., *Physics of the Aurora and Airglow*. Academic Press, 1961.

Hooper, J. E., and M. Scharff, *Cosmic Radiation*. Methuen, 1957.

Massey, H. S. W., and R. L. F. Boyd, *The Upper Atmosphere*. Hutchinson, 1960.

Ratcliffe, J. A., *Physics of the Upper Atmosphere*. Academic Press, 1960.

Mining and Minerals

Dobrin, Milton B., *Introduction to Geophysical Prospecting* (2nd ed.). McGraw-Hill, 1960.

Kraus, Edward H., Walter F. Hunt and Lewis S. Ramsdell, *Mineralogy* (5th ed.). McGraw-Hill, 1959.

Pearl, Richard M., *How to Know the Minerals and Rocks*. McGraw-Hill, 1955.

Witcombe, Wallace H., *All About Mining*. Longmans, Green, 1937.

Weather and Climate

Battan, Louis J., *The Nature of Violent Storms*. Doubleday, New York, 1961.

Byers, Horace Roberts, *General Meteorology* (3rd ed.). McGraw-Hill, 1959.

*Clausse, Roger, and Léopold Facy, trans. by J. Ferrante, *The Clouds*. Grove Press: Evergreen Books, 1961.

Fairbridge, Rhodes W., ed., *Solar Variation, Climatic Change, and Related Geophysical Problems*. New York Academy of Sciences, 1961.

Fisher, Robert Moore, *How to Know and Predict the Weather*. New American Library, New York, 1960.

Kendrew, W. G., *The Climates of the Continents* (4th ed.). Oxford University Press, 1953.

Lehr, Paul E., R. Will Burnett and Herbert S. Zim, *Weather*. Golden Press, New York, 1957.

Loebsack, Theo, *Earth's Envelope*. Collins, 1959.

*Orr, Clyde, Jr., *Between Earth and Space*. Macmillan, New York, 1959.

Petterssen, Sverre, *Introduction to Meteorology* (2nd ed.). McGraw-Hill, 1958.

Shapley, Harlow, ed., *Climatic Change: Evidence, Causes, and Effects*. Harvard University Press: Oxford University Press, 1954.

Fossils and Evolution

Aitken, M. J., *Physics and Archeology*. Interscience, New York, 1961.

* Colbert, Edwin H., *Evolution of the Vertebrates*. John Wiley, 1955.

Fenton, Carroll Lane, and Mildred Adams Fenton, *The Fossil Book*. Doubleday: W. H. Allen, 1963.

Libby, Willard F., *Radiocarbon Dating* (2nd ed.). University of Chicago Press, 1955.

† Matthews, William H., *Fossils: An Introduction to Prehistoric Life*. Constable, 1962.

Romer, Alfred S., *Vertebrate Paleontology* (2nd ed.). University of Chicago Press, 1945.

Shrock, Robert R., and William H. Twenhofel, *Principles of Invertebrate Paleontology*. McGraw-Hill, 1953.

Stirton, R. A., *Time, Life, and Man: The Fossil Record*. John Wiley, 1959.

Young, J. Z., *The Life of Vertebrates*. Oxford University Press, 1950.

General

Academy of Sciences of the U.S.S.R., trans. by J. B. Sykes, *The Other Side of the Moon*. Pergamon Press, 1960.

* Adams, Frank Dawson, *The Birth and Development of the Geological Sciences*. Dover: Constable, 1954.

Asimov, Isaac, *The Intelligent Man's Guide to Science* (Vol. 1, *The Physical Sciences*). Basic Books, New York, 1960.

Baker, Robert H. *Astronomy* (7th ed.). D. Van Nostrand, 1959.

Bascom, Willard, *A Hole in the Bottom of the Sea*. Weidenfeld & Nicholson, 1961.

* Bates, D. R., ed., *The Planet Earth*. Pergamon Press, 1957.

Crombie, Alistair C., *Medieval and Early Modern Science* (2nd rev. ed., 2 vols.). Doubleday, New York, 1959.

† Dury, G. H., *The Face of the Earth*. Penguin Books, 1959.

* Fenton, Carroll Lane, and Mildred Adams Fenton, *Giants of Geology*. Doubleday: W. H. Allen, 1962.

† Hurley, Patrick M., *How Old Is the Earth?* Heinemann, 1960.

Kendrick, Sir T., *The Lisbon Earthquake*. Methuen, 1956.

Krauskopf, Konrad, and Arthur Beiser, *The Physical Universe* (2nd ed.). McGraw-Hill, 1967.

Larousse Encyclopedia of the Earth. Hamlyn, 1961.

LIFE Editorial Staff and Lincoln Barnett, *The World We Live In*. Time Inc., New York, 1955.

Moore, Ruth, *The Coil of Life*. Constable, 1961.

The Planet Earth. A Scientific American book, Simon & Schuster, New York, 1957.

Richardson, Robert S., and Chesley Bonestell, *Man and the Moon*. World Publishing, New York, 1961.

Stumpff, Karl, *The Planet Earth*. University of Michigan Press: Mayflower, 1959.

Sullivan, Walter, *Assault on the Unknown: The International Geophysical Year*. Hodder & Stoughton, 1962.

Thompson, William L., and others, eds., *Man's Role in Changing the Face of the Earth*. University of Chicago Press, 1956.

True, Webster P., ed., *Smithsonian Treasury of Science* (3 vols.). Simon & Schuster, New York, 1960.

Whitrow, G. J., *Structure and Evolution of the Universe* (rev. ed.). Hutchinson, 1959.

Wilkins, Hugh Percival, and Patrick Moore, *The Moon*. Faber & Faber, 1955.

Wilson, J. Tuzo, *IGY: The Year of the New Moons*. Michael Joseph, 1961.

* Available in Great Britain in a paperback edition.

† Available only in a paperback edition.

Where The Earth's Land Forms May Be Seen

Striking geological formations are to be found in many areas of the world. Many of these are readily accessible to visitors. Some of the most unusual of these formations are singled out and described below.

Volcanoes

On the European continent, active volcanoes exist only in the extreme north and south. The North American continent has them in Alaska and the Younger mountain ranges of the West. They are also to be seen in great profusion throughout the Pacific Isles.

VESUVIUS, CENTRAL ITALY: Probably the best known of all volcanoes, Vesuvius erupted in A.D. 79 after a long period of dormancy, burying the towns of Pompeii and Herculaneum near Naples. The last major eruption, which occurred in 1944, completely devastated the town of San Sebastiano.

MOUNT ETNA, SICILY: Etna's eruptions, although less volatile, occur more frequently than those of Vesuvius. The slopes of this volcano are studded with numerous eruptive cones. But since the lava soil makes the area a highly fertile one, these slopes are densely populated.

ICELAND: This island (103,000 square kilometres in area) is made up entirely of volcanic material, namely lava, pumice stones, volcanic tuff and ashes. Thirty volcanoes are still active; of these, Hekla and Askja are the most significant.

HAWAII, U.S.A.: Occupying more than three hundred square miles on the islands of Hawaii and Maui, the Hawaii National Park includes the 13,680-foot active shield volcano, Mauna Loa, and the near-by crater of Kilauea, which last erupted in 1960. Maui's outstanding feature is the vast dormant crater of Haleakala.

KATMAI, ALASKA, U.S.A.: Within this volcanic range, some ninety miles long, are fumaroles in the Valley of 10,000 Smokes, crater lakes and cones; Katmai also has a giant *caldera*, which is the basin formed when the volcano erupted and collapsed in 1912.

YELLOWSTONE NATIONAL PARK, U.S.A.: This is a park of volcanic superlatives. It has the world's largest and most spectacular collection of geysers (about 200), thousands of hot springs, mud volcanoes and fumaroles, Obsidian Cliff and petrified trees.

Faults and Folds

Faults are natural fractures which occur in the crust of the earth. When this crust is pressed up and down along these faults by diastrophism, the earth's surface is squeezed into folded layers and entire areas are wrenched askew.

THE UPPER RHINE GRABEN, GERMANY: This is the large rift valley located within a long range of weaknesses spanning an area of the earth's crust between the Mediterranean Sea and Lake Mjösen in Norway. In this valley, the interior of the Graben has been depressed several thousand metres since the Eocene Age.

THE HARZ MOUNTAINS, GERMANY: The northern borders of these mountains form a long thrust zone along which the Palaeozoic Harz Mountains have been pressed against and on top of their foreland. The overall effect of this action is that the younger strata on the mountains have been straightened out and steepened.

THE ALPS: Movements of immense rock masses across distances of more than sixty miles have taken place in the Alps. The Western Alps are especially rich in these phenomena (known as nappes) in which older strata may lie on top of younger ones, frequently in repetition.

ZION NATIONAL PARK, UTAH, U.S.A.: One of the most vivid proofs of the mobility of the earth's crust is to be seen in the North Western part of the United States. Disrupted by the great Hurricane Fault, the brilliantly coloured canyons along Kolob Terrace dramatically illustrate the effects of up-lifting, faulting and erosion.

Sedimentation

The accumulated layers of sediment laid down by oceans, lakes and rivers form the stone records from which geologists read the past. The world is rich in these, but the most outstanding sequences of sedimentary rock, covering 1,500 million years of the earth's history, are found in the first three areas listed below, all within seventy-five miles of one another.

GRAND CANYON, ARIZONA, U.S.A.: The earth's timetable is revealed here. The canyon contains 1,270 million years of stratification; the deepest layer dates from 1,500 million years ago, and the most recent from the Mesozoic era.

ZION NATIONAL PARK, UTAH, U.S.A.: Sharply defined, these strata were formed during the Mesozoic era, 230 to 63 million years ago.

BRYCE CANYON, UTAH, U.S.A.: The exposed layers in this canyon show geologic history dating back 63 million years.

NORTH SEA FORMATIONS: In the tidal flats of the North Sea, the formations of recent sediments are apparent in the form of banks and islands. The best known of these is Dogger Bank, an area of over 11,000 square miles, which has often proved a hazardous problem for navigation.

Erosion

The forces of water and ice, weather and wind, constantly wearing away the earth, have created many odd and beautiful effects inland and on sea-shores throughout the world. Among these are the earth's greatest canyon and largest natural bridge, castellated spires, vast caves and beautifully sculptured coast lines.

GRAND CANYON, ARIZONA, U.S.A.: This canyon without equal, cut by the river Colorado, is four to eighteen miles wide, two hundred and seventeen miles long, and four thousand to six thousand feet deep.

RAINBOW BRIDGE, UTAH, U.S.A.: The record 309-foot span soars two hundred and seventy eight feet above the stream that scooped it out.

MAMMOTH CAVE, KENTUCKY, U.S.A.: No one is certain how big this eroded limestone cave really is, but one hundred and fifty miles of it have been explored. Distributed over its five levels are three rivers, eight waterfalls and two lakes.

EASTERN ATLANTIC COAST: Cliffs and stacks have been carved by pounding waves all along the Atlantic shore from the western end of the Pyrenees up to Britanny, Ireland, Scotland and Norway to the North Cape. This action has given the coastline such wonders as Mont St. Michel in France, Land's End in England and the fjords in Norway.

HELIGOLAND: This island off the north-west coast of Germany is formed of bundsandstein rock and is the last remnant of an ancient plateau which had a much greater surface area.

KARST MOUNTAINS, YUGOSLAVIA: These boast all the impressive features of the "karst"—clints, dolines (sinks), poljes, sand-pipes, extensive systems of caverns with drip-stones, and "karst" springs.

Glaciation

Huge rivers of ice which show evidence of present or past motion

cover 5.8 million square miles, or 10% of the earth's surface—an area almost the size of the South American continent.

GLACIER BAY, ALASKA, U.S.A.: In an area of nearly 3,600 square miles, there are some twenty giant glaciers and scores of smaller ones. These show glaciation in various stages from the rapid flow of Muir Glacier (twenty or thirty feet a day) through stagnant ice masses to fjords.

JOSTEDALSBRAE, NORWAY: This is the largest single glacier in Europe located in the Norwegian Chains. It covers an area of 940 square kilometres and has no less than twenty-four glacier tongues.

ALETSCH, SWITZERLAND: The largest glacier in the Alps flows off the Jungfrau complex of mountains and is twenty-seven kilometres long.

NORTHERN GERMANY: Northern Germany contains many interesting examples of the effects of Pleistocene glaciation. In certain places, the moraines and gravels covering older sediments are more than 300 feet thick.

Fossils

The fossil remains and imprints of plants and animals that lived as long ago as 500 million years are clearly preserved and visible in sedimentary rocks throughout the world.

DINOSAUR, UTAH-COLORADO, U.S.A.: This is the finest dinosaur deposit in the world. The specimens range in size from the 84-foot diplodocus through the brontosaurus and allosaurus to the relatively small (six foot) laosaurus. One wall in the Visitors' Centre consists of a huge section of fossil-bearing rock. Here it is possible to observe the excavation and preparation of fossil skeletons.

PETRIFIED FOREST, ARIZONA, U.S.A.: This is the world's largest and most colourful collection of fossilized wood, dating from the Triassic period, 230 to 200 million years ago.

HOLZMADEN, GERMANY: Here excavations of the "Posidonia" shales of the Upper Liassic Age are revealing a rich deposit of fossils. Most well done are the wonderfully preserved skeletons of the ichthyosaurus, where all the details of their bones are still well defined; often impressions of the skin covering the bones are equally clear.

PARIS BASIN, FRANCE: Paris Basin contains some of the best examples of Eocene fossils, both vertebrates and invertebrates. This area has been well known for this since the very beginning of the science of palaeontology.

Credits

The sources for the illustrations in this book are shown below. Credits for pictures from left to right are separated by commas, top to bottom by dashes.

Cover—Ray Manley from Shostal
8—Frank J. Scherschel
10, 11—Joseph Bertelli
12, 13—Joseph M. Sedacca courtesy American Museum of Natural History
14—Matt Greene
17—NASA
18 to 21—Antonio Petruccelli
22—Herman Eisenbeiss from Photo Researchers, Inc.
23—Don Moss, Emil Schulthess from Black Star
24—*Top* Lewis C. Thomas and Joseph F. Ossanna Jr. from The Bell Telephone Laboratories, Inc., Murray Hill, New Jersey; *bottom* Don Moss
25—Emil Schulthess from Black Star
26, 27—NASA
28—U.S. Air Force
29—NASA
30—William A. Cassidy-Lamont Geological Observatory—The Smithsonian Institution—Jack Birns
31—The Smithsonian Institution, courtesy American Museum of Natural History (2)—Albert Fenn
32, 33—*Left* Jay Leviton; *right* Professor L. Kulik—J. R. Eyerman
34—Andreas Feininger
36, 37—Joseph M. Sedacca courtesy American Museum of Natural History
39—Adolph E. Brotman
40—John Woods
43—Adolph E. Brotman
45—Mel Hunter
46, 47—*Left* Charles W. Halgren courtesy Caru Studios—Camera Hawaii from Alpha Photo Associates, Inc.; *right* Eliot Elisofon
48—New York University Engineering Research Division
49—J. R. Eyerman
50, 51—*The New York Times*, courtesy International Seismological Summary—John Woods—Joseph Lynch S. J.
52, 53—*Left* Hugo Benioff courtesy California Institute of Technology-Seismological Lab-

oratory—Carnegie Institution of Washington; *centre* Carl Mydans; *right* N. R. Farbman —Mainichi Shimbun
54—Larry Lauve, Scripps Institution of Oceanography
55—Fritz Goro
56—Mel Coston for Humble Oil and Refining Company
58, 59—Dan Todd
60—Dan Todd—Matt Greene
61—Dan Todd—Matt Greene
65—Roland B. Bourne
66—Max Gschwind for FORTUNE
67—N. R. Farbman
68, 69—D. J. K. O'Connell
70, 71—The Reverend Frank Dinwiddie, C. R. Rouillon © World Meteorological Organization, Ruth Galaid from Photo Researchers, Inc., Russ Kinne from Photo Researchers, Inc.—Eliot Elisofon
72—Richard Jepperson from Alpha Photos
73—Ewing Galloway
74, 75—*Left* U.S. Naval Ordnance Laboratory—Horace S. Benson courtesy General Electric Corporation; *centre* Ted Bank from Monkmeyer Press Photos; *right* Wide World Photos
76, 77—*Left* Bill Burkett—United Press International; *right* George Yates for *The Des Moines Register*
78, 79—Air Force Cambridge Research Laboratories, Charles W. Banks for Boston *Globe*
80—J. Allan Cash
83—Dan Todd
84, 85—George V. Kelvin
88—Adolph E. Brotman
91—Margaret Bourke-White
92—Stan Wayman—Andreas Feininger
93—Earl Palmer from Monkmeyer Press Photos
94—Margaret Bourke-White—Bob Landry
95—Margaret Bourke-White—Homer Page for FORTUNE
96—Margaret Bourke-White
97—Edmund B. Gerard
98—George Silk

99—J. R. Eyerman—Fritz Goro
100—Courtesy American Museum of Naval History, Dmitri Kessel—Dmitri Kessel, courtesy American Museum of Natural History—Dmitri Kessel
101—Dmitri Kessel, courtesy American Museum of Natural History—courtesy American Museum of Natural History, Russ Kinne from Photo Researchers, Inc.—Floyd R. Getsinger, Dmitri Kessel
192—Andreas Feininger—Ultra-Violet Products, Inc. courtesy Gemmological Institute of America, Floyd R. Getsinger
103—Floyd R. Getsinger
104—Cole Weston from Rapho Guillumette
109, 111—Matt Greene
113—David Muench
114—Andreas Feininger
115—Josef Muench—Nino Carbe
116, 117—Ansel Adams from Magnum
118, 119—Ernst Haas from Magnum, George Leavens from Photo Researchers, Inc.—Paul Jensen, Josef Muench (3)
120—Ansel Adams from Magnum
121—A. Y. Owen—Andreas Feininger
122, 123—Ned Haines from Rapho Guillumette
124—Margaret Bourke-White
125—KLM Royal Dutch Airlines
126, 126—N. R. Farbman, Fritz Goro
128, 129—Royal Canadian Air Force and The Arctic Institute of North America, William M. Lee
130—John H. Gerard from Monkmeyer Press Photos
132, 133—Adolph E. Brotman
134, 135—Mark A. Binn
138, 139—Maps by Adolph E. Brotman
141—Carroll Lane and Mildred Adams Fenton
142—National Park Service
143—Carroll Lane and Mildred Adams Fenton—courtesy F. M. Carpenter
144, 145—Antonio Petruccelli

146—Dr. George Claus and Dr. Bartholomew Nagi
147—United Press International —Shuhei Yuyama courtesy Dr. Sidney Fox
148, 149—*Left* Albert Fenn— Kodak Research Laboratories; *right* Ezra Stoller for Sloan-Kettering Institute
150—Councilman Morgan, M.D. Department of Microbiology, Columbia University
151—From *Electron Microscopy* by Dr. Ralph W. G. Wyckoll © 1949 by Interscience Publishers Division of John Wiley and Sons, C. E. Hall—courtesy Dr. Ralph W. G. Wyckoff and The Upjohn Company, Kalamazoo, Michigan
152—Dr. Roman Vishniac—Fritz Goro
153—Dr. Roman Vishniac—Fritz Goro
154—Ezra Stoller (ESTO)
155—Jerry Cooke
156—Argonne National Lab— Hansel Mieth
157—Dr. Arnold H. Sparrow and Robert F. Smith—Brookhaven National Laboratory
158—Mel Hunter
163, 164—Alex Ebel
167—Marc Riboud from Magnum
168, 169—Thomas E. Benner from Shostal—John Dominis
170, 171—Laurence Lowry from Rapho Guillumette, Jerry Cooke
172—Marshall Lockman from Black Star—Howard Sochurek
173—A. Y. Owen
174, 175—Map by Fred Freeman
176—Albert Fenn
177—Joe Scherschel, N. R. Farbman
178—U.S. Signal Corps—George Burns courtesy General Electric Company
179—Fritz Goro
180, 181—*Left* Andreas Feininger; *top right* Larry Burrows
182—NASA
183—United Press International
186, 187—Matt Greene

Acknowledgments

The editors of this book are indebted to Orson L. Anderson, Professor of Geology, Lamont-Doherty Geological Observatory, Columbia University; Hugo Benioff, Asst. Professor of Seismology, California Institute of Technology; Cesare Emiliani, Research Assoc. Professor of Marine Geology, Marine Laboratory, U. of Miami; William R. Farrand, Asst. Professor of Geology, and Councilman Morgan, Assoc. Professor of Microbiology, College of Physicians and Surgeons, Columbia University; Gerard P. Kuiper, Director, W. J. McDonald Observatory, U. of Texas; the Reverend J. Joseph Lynch, head of the Seismic Station, Fordham University; Gordon J. F. MacDonald, Professor of Geophysics, U. of California; Brian Mason, Curator, Physical Geology and Mineralogy, and Norman D. Newell, Curator, Inverte-

brate Fossils and Historical Geology, American Museum of Natural History; Brian J. O'Brien, Asst. Professor of Physics and Astronomy, U. of Iowa; Robert H. Rose and Howard R. Stagner, National Park Service, U.S. Department of the Interior; Jerome Spar, Assoc. Professor of Meteorology, New York University; Herbert Becker, Chief of Structural Sciences, Aracon Labs; Erling Dorf, Professor of Geology and Paleobotany, Princeton University; Melvin Calvin, Professor of Chemistry, U. of California; Sidney Fox, Professor of Chemistry, Florida State University; Thomas Gold, Professor of Astronomy, Cornell University; J. Lamar Worzel, Asst. Director, and J. Laurence Kulp, Professor of Geochemistry and Director of the Geochemistry Laboratory, Lamont-Doherty Geological Observatory, Columbia University.

Index

Numerals in italics indicate a photograph or painting of the subject mentioned.

XXXXXXXXXX

Typesetting by C. E. Dawkins (Typesetters) Ltd., London, S.E.1
Smeets Lithographers, Weert, Printed in Holland
Bound by Proost en Brandt N.V., Amsterdam